Best

COME ON, GRANDDAD, HOLD MY HAND

Edward Gwa
Haworth
21/5/17

COME ON, GRANDDAD, HOLD MY HAND

Edward Evans

First published in Great Britain in 2012 by
Worthside Holdings Ltd
Worthside House
2 Belle Isle Road
Haworth
West Yorkshire, BD22 8QQ

Typesetting in Meridien by
Set Systems, Gresham Court, Station Approach, Wendens Ambo CB11 4LG

Printed in Great Britain by Grosvenor Group.

A catalogue record for this book is available from the British Library.

ISBN 978-0-9571252-7-8

Dedication

This book is dedicated to our dear friends of forty years, Alan and Margaret Waterhouse, who are facing the trauma of seeing Alan suffer with this dreadful Alzheimer's disease. It is only when you become close to it that you truly understand the difficulties families face when confronted by a member suffering from the disease.

You see a loved one change into a totally different person from the one you knew and loved. They seem like a complete stranger and yet they are still the same person; the only difference is they have become ill with no chance at the moment of getting better.

I also dedicate this book to all the families that have been struck by this crippling disease, because now I know what you are all going through. I know what you are all suffering and I know you need every bit of help and love you can get.

Acknowledgements

I would once again like to thank my lovely wife Lilian for the hours of reading undertaken in the process of correcting my terrible grammar before I had the courage to send the manuscript to Kay Gale, my editor, who also did sterling work in preparing this book for publication.

I would also like to thank Jill Buchanan, my timeless reader and our friend, who also put in hours of reading time, finding faults when we would have thought there were no more to be found, and for her constructive criticism which I could not do without.

However!

Before you read my story I want you to read this poem sent to me by a friend who is aware of how I feel for those suffering with this dreadful disease. It epitomizes everything that we all need to be aware of; not only the people who care but those of us who never give a thought.

It is one of the loveliest poems I have ever read. It is moving, heartfelt and real and it is a prelude to my story. This is how it was sent to me.

Cranky Old Man

When an old man died in the geriatric ward of a nursing home in an Australian country town, it was believed he had nothing left of any value.

Later when the nurses were going through his meagre possessions, they found this poem. Its quality and content so impressed the staff that copies were made and distributed to every nurse in the hospital.

One nurse took her copy to Melbourne, where the old man's sole bequest to posterity has appeared in Christmas editions of magazines around the country and also in magazines for mental health. A slide presentation has been made based on his simple but eloquent poem, and this old man with nothing left to give to the world is now the author of this anonymous poem winging across the internet.

Cranky Old Man

What do you see nurses? . . .	what do you see?
What are you thinking . . .	When you're looking at me?
A cranky old man . . .	not very wise,
Uncertain of habit . . .	with far away eyes.
Who dribbles his food . . .	and makes no reply
When you say in a loud voice . . .	'I do wish you'd try.'
Who seems not to notice . . .	the things that you do
And forever is losing . . .	a sock or a shoe.
Who, resisting or not . . .	lets you do as you will
With bathing and feeding . . .	the long day to fill.
Is that what you're thinking? . . .	Is that what you see?
Then open your eyes nurse . . .	you're not looking at me.
I'll tell you who I am . . .	as I sit there so still,
As I do at your bidding . . .	as I eat at your will.
I'm a small child of ten . . .	with a father and mother,
Brothers and sisters . . .	who love one another.
A young boy of sixteen . . .	with wings on his feet,
Dreaming that soon now . . .	a lover he'll meet.
A groom soon at twenty . . .	my heart gives a leap,
Remembering the news . . .	that I promised to keep.

At twenty five now . . . I have young of my own,
Who need me to guide . . . and a secure happy home,
A man of thirty . . . my young now grown fast,
Bound to each other . . . with ties that should last.

At forty my young sons . . . have grown and are gone,
But my woman is beside me . . . to see I don't mourn.
At fifty once more . . . babies play 'round my knee
Again we know children . . . my loved one and me.

Dark days are upon me . . . my wife is now dead.
I look to the future . . . I shudder with dread.
For my young are all rearing . . . young of their own.
And I think of the years . . . and the love that I've known.

I'm now an old man . . . and nature is cruel.
It's jest to make old age . . . look like a fool.
The body, it crumbles . . . grace and vigour depart.
There is now a stone . . . where I once had a heart.

But inside this old carcass . . . a young man still dwells
And now and again . . . my battered heart swells.
I remember the joys . . . I remember the pain,
And I'm loving and living . . . life over again.

I think of the years, all too few . . . gone too fast,
And accept the stark fact . . . that nothing can last.
So open your eyes people . . . open and see
Not a cranky old man.
Look closer . . . See . . . ME!!!!!

Anonymous and still wonderful.

Chapter 1

Oh God! Here comes Sister and what a lovely surprise – she's brought the Dragon with her. I'll act dumb, at least that will cheer me up.

'He seems to be very comfortable and has settled in well,' the Sister said to the Dragon.

'Hasn't he got a lovely smile, he's in a world of his own you know, just sitting there. I don't think he knows you or anyone for that matter. Anyway go on through,' the nurse told them.

No I bloody haven't. I hate the place. I know it's better than the last, but I want to go home. And of course I know everyone, you silly cow. I just don't want to know her, my bloody wife, the Dragon. She's the one who dumped me in here just to get rid of me and I'll never forget the bloody place before. I was spoiling her life. I was in the way and now I have been dumped in here, because she can't manage, not even for a short time whilst Constance, my friend and carer, gets better. It feels like I have been in here for years, but it's only two weeks.

She didn't want to come and see me before, so why now? Someone must have done something, or said something.

Oh thank god she's brought the children.

'Come on say hello to Granddad. Quickly, we haven't much time.'

Bloody hell, they've only just come. 'It's Elizabeth and Max.' God I've said it – Elizabeth and Max, I've remembered.

'See Grandma, he does know us, don't you Granddad?'

'Of course I do.' See you bitch, I haven't gone entirely loopy.

1

'Now tell Granddad what you have been doing at school,'

I held out my hands and clutched Elizabeth's gently in mine and just listened; tears began running down my cheeks as she told me everything in an excited manner, as though she had to tell it quickly in case she forgot. 'That's wonderful,' I said. Then Max began relating his adventures. He got a star for good work. My, he's the one with the brains; he will be the businessman, just like his granddad, but please don't end up like me Max.

'Come on you two, don't make Granddad too tired, he needs his rest and we've got to go now.'

Bloody hell! Stay a little longer, for heaven's sake; I do nothing but rest, looking into space, waiting for someone to come and talk to me and not at me or about me as if I'm not there. 'Stay a little longer, please,' I said.

'Don't be silly, Granddad; the children have got to get home.'

I leaned over and whispered in Elizabeth's ear, 'Ask Grandma if I can come home.' But I knew it was a futile effort as I was in the way.

'Granddad wants to know if he can come home.'

'When he's better,' the Dragon said impatiently. 'Come on now you two, time to go'

Go on then, duty done, you don't have to bother for another two weeks. You can stay away, but please not the children.

I remember holding on to that little girl as if it was for the last time, I didn't want her to go. She had so much life in her I just wanted a part of it; to come back for a few more years, to see them grow up. Now I have to treat every time as my last as I never know when oblivion will come.

''Bye Granddad, See you soon.'

''Bye sweetheart. Yes, please come and see me soon,' I added, the tears once again returning

'Granddad's crying, Grandma.'

'Oh, he's just being silly, aren't you, dear?'

Don't dear me you bloody evil woman.

2

'Well we must be going, Sister, we don't want to overtire him, do we children?'

They didn't answer but I could see the disappointment in their eyes.

'We'll see you again soon, Mrs Stephens,' Sister said, but there was no response from the Dragon, who simply breezed out as unconcernedly as she had breezed in.

They had left and I had gone back to my silence and my thoughts only to be disturbed by Sister. Oh god, there's two of them this time, what are they going to do now?

'Now then, David, did we enjoy seeing our visitors?'

What a bloody silly question. I would enjoy seeing Attila the Hun, if he would stay and talk to me. Anyway, who's we and they're my visitors, except her; you can have her, but the little ones are mine.

'Come on, David, let's be having you. You've got to be doing your number two's and then we've got to be giving you a wash, before we put you to bed, haven't we?' Sister Dorking said somewhat patronizingly to me, her patient. 'Nurse just grab hold of his arm and help me lift him.'

They think I'm bloody daft, deaf and crippled and I'm not. All that's wrong with me is I forget things. Can you imagine what it's like to be treated like this when everything has been so good? To be taken to the toilet and waited for, whilst you did a wee or had a crap and then had your backside wiped by some little girl or boy? I can do it on my own, but sometimes I forget.

'There you are, David, all done and dusted; now, let's get you into bed'

Oh, I wish I could get people to understand that I do know what's going on. I wish I could tell everyone that my mind is OK, but I just can't get my brain to be normal. I know I've got dementia, and possibly Alzheimer's has caused that and right from the beginning, he told me so.

Who told me, I can't remember. Think, man, think. I have to keep thinking or I might lose that.

Who the hell told me? Of course, James did. James Percival, my doctor.

See, you can do it.

That's my problem, I forget things, what I said a minute or two ago, sometimes where I live, sometimes what I have done, sometimes how to eat and even sometimes how to go to the toilet.

I can get lost in my own home, even when I'm just going to the toilet.

I know that I often repeat myself, it just comes out. I'll tell the same story two or three times.

Not every time, as sometimes I slip back into gear and I can be almost normal and sometimes I can even speak; but I know it's getting worse and I think even my mind will eventually go.

They think I don't know what the problem is, especially her, my BLOODY WIFE; she's the one who dumped me in here, a bloody nursing home. But I do understand. I may not be able to communicate, but I do understand, every little bloody thing.

She's told everyone she needs a rest, she can't cope with me anymore, and everybody feels sorry for her. I remember she tried it before. I had arranged for twenty-four-hour care with two nurses all the time, and what did she do with them? Only told them they're not needed and while Constance and Hannah were away she dumped me in a home miles away and got me certified, which nearly finished me. They even tried to kill my memory to keep me in there, and if it hadn't been for Hannah I don't know where I would be, and all this just to get her hands on the family money. She hasn't done anything; she's just there giving orders to the nurses and to my carers and she can't even put up with that.

But what about me? Where's the 'for better or for worse'? She's only had a few months of this, but what about me? They have all forgotten the forty years I spent in a job that for twenty of those years I hated and I never told anyone. I could have run away every bloody day of the week but I didn't, I had to think of her and the children. I never had any life of my own. Now look at them, her and four bloody kids; well, three of them at least, and now I'm a bloody embarrassment to them all and they want to leave me in here.

But she's got a bloody shock to come. She thinks the kids will look after her, but they won't. They're all too bloody selfish. Mind you, I've always said they've got their own lives to lead and we didn't have children to be our servants.

Well, I can understand. I may not be able to communicate all the time, but my mind inside seems to be working; although I know even that's getting worse. Oh my god, I'm even repeating things to myself.

It's only half past bloody five and they want us out of the way so we have to go to bed. Well, I have a window to look out of, better than some of the poor buggers; it's one of the advantages of being reasonably well off and I've got a better room. At least I can think about the good times.

'Look, nurse, there's that smile again,' Sister said. 'He's gone back into his little world.'

Of course I have. I've got something to smile about. The family – and that includes my children, apart from Hannah – have had me certified or sectioned, hoping to prove I am incapable of making a decision and that I am a danger to myself and others. I was rescued from the last one, but they are having me reassessed in a day or so. I know they want to get their hands on my money, which is a considerable amount, and then I will be left to rot, probably put in some cheap nursing home, until I die, like the one Phoebe, the bloody Dragon, put me in before. They really will be in for a surprise when they find out what I have done.

My father never really took to Phoebe and I know he felt she was just after the family money, so, as a consequence of this, I drew up an airtight prenuptial agreement. Initially, it was simply to protect the business as we had gone public and didn't want to risk the shares going outside the family should she divorce me at a later date. Phoebe could see the advantages she would gain by joining the family and as soon as she saw the monthly allowance she would receive she quickly signed the agreement with no questions.

It's one of the few things that have kept me going, thinking about what I have done. I must have been a devious bastard, or perhaps sensible, but deep down I knew they would try something, so the moment I knew I had the start of this terrible disease and whilst I was still of sound mind, I went to see the family doctor and friend and he organised for two totally independent neurologists, one psychiatrist and an independent lawyer, non-other than the local president of the law society, to assess me in order to protect me against my family and other abuse. I made a good allowance for my wife, which now I regret, and the rest was to be used to look after me.

'David, what on earth are you laughing at?' Sister asked, having heard me make an unusual noise. I would have loved to have told her, but it would have spoiled the surprise, so I just ignored her and carried on staring. It was the easiest way to get rid of her.

I was put in this home, miles out of the way, and deliberately left there in the hope I would deteriorate quickly. Mental torture I would call it. They, that is Phoebe, my wife, simply wanted to hasten on my dementia and I believe if I had remained there for much longer they would have succeeded; but now, with better care, I could feel my senses returning and I began thinking how it had all happened.

I remember I was sent to boarding school and did rather well at the three R's; I was a good sportsman too, played cricket and rugby for the school and was in the athletics team. Now I have to get help to go to the bogs in case I forget where I am. They occasionally help me get dressed in the morning, wash me, bathe me and sometimes even have to help me feed myself. What a bloody existence! See my problem – I cannot stick to the subject.

I wasn't a bad-looking chap. I discovered girls at an early age and was lucky enough to have Phoebe Western, the school sweetheart, as my girlfriend. She was everybody's dream; well, the boys' that is, and as she grew older, she grew more beautiful and developed curves in all the right places. I was lucky, but I was also too possessive; Phoebe knew she was good looking and wanted to play the field. I remember when she finished with me, I was devastated, but my mother said, 'You're a good-looking lad and there are plenty of other fish in the sea.' There were, but I wanted Phoebe. It became worse for me when I went to Bristol University and she went to Bath and for some awful reason we kept bumping into each other. It always caused a flutter in my heart when I saw her, but I was playing the field too and like all young men, one soon forgets the past.

I qualified with a BSc and began working for an engineering company in my home town, whilst Phoebe disappeared and did not complete her final year at Bath; rumour had it she was expecting a child and left to have an abortion.

Gosh! I've suddenly thought, was this the beginning of my troubles? I was in my twenties and I remember there was no way I wanted to live at home with my parents; not that I wasn't fond of them, I just wanted my freedom and I managed to get a flat on the edge of the town centre. It had two bedrooms, a kitchen, which I never used, as we always had plenty of volunteers. I say we as James would often stay for the weekend, as he had a further year to do at university for his medical degree, and I also had plenty of lodgers. It was a regular little den of iniquity, but what's life all about when I can end up like this? At least I can say I have done something with my life.

Anyway, I remember having a late-night discussion with my boss Frank Payne and an expert from Holland about various problems the firm was experiencing with some Dutch mechanical parts. It wasn't the most stimulating subject matter for a Friday evening, especially when I had Paula Smith waiting for me as we were supposed to be going to the pictures. She at least acted as our hostess, supplying endless alcoholic drinks, teas, coffees and toast and even went out for fish and chips for us.

We did manage to sort out all our problems before they left at about three in the morning. I was too tired for anything else and went straight to bed dragging a shattered Paula with me.

The following morning I can remember feeling strange, as though I was lost, and I found myself wandering to the lounge. There were papers and drawings everywhere.

'What the hell's this?' I shouted. 'We've been burgled.'

Paula came running in and on seeing the mess, calmly said, 'No, we haven't, that's how we left it.'

'Left what?'

'The mess. You didn't finish till gone three and we went straight to bed.'

'Finished what?

'David, you had a meeting with Frank.'

'Oh yes, I remember.' I replied, but I didn't really, I couldn't remember anything of the meeting and it wasn't until I read through the notes and papers and questioned Paula throughout the day that I began to recall what had happened. It was quite frightening; I seemed to have completely lost seven or eight hours. I didn't discuss it with anybody, I was too embarrassed, but Paula did notice and for the next day or two she would ask me if I was all right.

She was a nice girl and I went about with her for a few months, but she soon tired of the meetings that seemed to develop frequently as Frank was becoming estranged from his wife and he turned to me for company.

I left Frank's company and joined Pennington's on a much greater salary than he could afford and began a very successful period of my working life. After two or three years I was offered a partnership in the business, which was named after my boss John Pennington. My father put up the money, to buy my way in, which I gladly accepted. He was a clever old thing and could see the opportunities that were out there and even invested extra money in the firm as it was short of cash to develop and grow. He actually took control but only as a sleeping partner and was never involved with the running of the firm; however, when John Pennington wanted to retire, my father bought him out to the mutual satisfaction of all parties and our family took control of the firm, with John Pennington staying on as consultant for a couple of years until I had learned enough to be more useful.

I had a wonderful social life as well as a thriving career, a beautiful old 1949 MG TC, which looked like new and which I adored. I even remember the number MZ 3643. I saw myself as an original eligible bachelor.

Remember Gloria Fenston? Of course I do; she was a very pretty woman who set her stall out for me. I took her out a few times and then one day I picked her up for lunch at the Old Sun in Haworth, which was way out into the country. We were having a pleasant meal when suddenly she disappeared under the table and wouldn't come up. I sat there in total amazement looking round wondering what to do. I lifted the tablecloth and looked underneath and there she was, looking at me in shock.

'What's the matter?' I asked, not knowing whether to laugh or cry with embarrassment. That was until she said, 'My husband has just come in with one of his clients.'

'You told me you were divorced.'

She just mouthed, I'm sorry.

I called the waiter over and explained the circumstances, asking him not to laugh, with me trying hard not to myself, which caused him even more difficulty in keeping a straight face.

'Right, sir, I know what we can do,' he replied, biting his lip to stop himself from laughing, and then he departed to the kitchen. I think the entire restaurant heard the burst of laughter when he shut the door behind him. I couldn't believe the next few minutes, it was pure farce.

Two members of staff returned with a screen, which they opened out, put by the table and then slowly walked holding the screen up whilst Gloria went out of the restaurant on all fours.

I gave the waiter a huge tip and we both had a good laugh.

I remember driving back home in absolute silence save for the occasional burst of laughter from me. I didn't see her again.

'David, you're still laughing; what's so funny?' Sister asked again
  'I was thinking about when I was young.' God I've told her.
  'Come on then, tell me what it's all about.'

'I was just young'

It's a strange thing, I can always remember things that happened years ago but sometimes I can't remember what happened a few minutes ago.

'Aren't you going to tell me?'

'No, they're thoughts just for me.'

'Oh, all right then.'

'Stay and talk, Sister. Please, we can talk about something else.'

'David I can't, I have work to do.'

Bugger you then, leave me alone. Now where was I? Sod it! I can't remember. Come on, think. You can do it.

I suppose I shouldn't have, but I did go out with some married women, the temptation was just too great to resist, particularly my secretary Philippa. She was a leggy blonde, built like Sabrina, and walked like Marilyn Monroe in *Some Like it Hot*. It's another day I shan't forget – but oh god, I suppose I will – anyway, we had been very busy during the day and as a thank you, I suggested we went out for an evening meal and then we went on into the country, miles from anywhere. Well, I suppose it was stupid to pull into this big muddy field, and when we had finished our love-making, I slipped the car into gear and found we were stuck. The more I tried, the deeper the car went in. There was nothing I could do except get out and push. Philippa got into the driving seat whilst I pushed. Of course, she was too heavy on the accelerator and you can imagine what I was like after the wheels spun throwing every little bit of mud in their way all over me. My feet were almost in water as the car sunk deeper every second those wheels turned. Philippa thought it was extremely funny until I explained what the options were. Either she pushed whilst I try to guide the car out, or we wait until the morning and got the farmer to tow us out. We sat in the car covered in mud for the whole night. It was cold and miserable and now I couldn't imagine anything worse than sitting in the car with your secretary for the whole night long. She couldn't say anything except, what are we going to do? What am I going to tell Roger? And I remember falling asleep listening to her constant moans. But worse was to come when I got out of the car in the early hours of the morning; the dawn was breaking and there was just enough daylight, for me to see where I was going so I began to walk to a nearby farm to try to get a tow, but who should I bump into? None other than our milkman. Not only did he supply our house but also the factory. How was I supposed to know he got his milk from this farm? You would have thought it was my fault when I told Philippa.

'Gerry! What brings you here?' I asked him.

'I might ask the same question,' he replied.

'Don't ask questions. I've got the MG stuck, can you tow me out?'

'I'll ask Fred to lend me the tractor; where are you?'

'About quarter of a mile down the road and don't you bloody dare say anything when you see the mess I'm in.'

Well, I remember Gerry and I stood on the back of the tractor, whilst Fred took us to the field. He didn't have to say anything; the two of them just burst out laughing and couldn't stop. Neither could I; it was either that or cry. There she was, the long-legged blonde in four-inch high-heeled shoes, short skirt up to her armpits, wrapped in a blanket, covered in mud, and trying to stamp her feet in temper because I had brought help in the shape of our milkman, and every time the foot went into the mud it came back shoeless. I never lived that down with Gerry and it wasn't blackmail that made me keep him as our milkman all these years.

My problem didn't end there. I had kept the engine running most of the night and after I had got back on the main road I ran out of petrol. There were no mobile phones in those days, so I had to find the nearest house and hope they had a telephone so that I could get some help. Thankfully they had and I telephoned the AA. They had motorbikes and sidecars in those days and when the patrolman arrived I know he tried not to laugh when he saw what condition Philippa and I were in. He tried desperately to hide his laughter but failed miserably, as it was impossible in the two-seater MG.

'Go off the road did you, sir?' he asked, although he clearly knew the answer already.

'You could say that,' I said, once again trying not to laugh.

Anyway, I remember I took Philippa straight back to her house and told her to tell her husband that we had a meeting in Worcester and that we went off the road. 'If he rings I'll tell him the same,' I told her. 'See you in the morning.'

'No you won't. I don't want to work for you any more' And that was that; she didn't turn up for work the next day and I never saw her again. *C'est la vie.*

Didn't I have a wonderful time? And then it was all ruined. Oh, I hate thinking about it, but yes, after all my philanderings who should come back on to the scene but Phoebe. Everybody knew she had been around a bit, had had loads of boyfriends and was still in demand. She still had the looks of a teenager and was very attractive, which meant she could pick and choose who she went out with. But she had begun to be materialistic and could tell simply by the size of the car the boys had, who had money. I should say young men as we were all in our twenties to thirties. I suppose there was a clique of us that would knock around together, party at each other's flats or meet for a drink in the local and at least once a month, particularly in the winter, go to a dinner and dance at one of the hotels. It was all very civilised. Several of my friends had been to public school and had developed an air of superiority, not nastily, I remember, but their local accent had disappeared, simply due to the fact that they had mixed with people from all areas, and it simply becomes a melange of various accents and could often sound posh.

It was these latter types that Phoebe was drawn to as they always appeared to be in the good jobs. They were managers of this or that, or in banking or professional people, where as I worked in a factory and I still had my old MG, not one of the new sleek Jags or Astons.

It often used to annoy me as I, or James who was still in training and could ill afford a round of drinks, seemed to always be first at the bar, and when we were paying it was always gin and tonics, but when it came to their turn it was half a bitter.

We did have some lovely times, but as time went on the friends began to grow up and the casual affairs became engagements and one by one couples married. I do remember Philip Daniels's wedding. He was the first of our group to tie the knot and of course he had a riotous stag party. We tied him to a lamp post whilst he was blind drunk, with the time and the address of the church where he was getting married attached to him, inviting the general public to release him and take him there, but they didn't. It was only when the best man realised he hadn't seen him that the search began. The wedding by this time was only an hour away. No one thought for one moment that he would still be tied up outside Marks and Spencers in the centre of the town, where hundreds would have passed, and it was only when someone decided to go and check that he was found, still the worse for wear. No one had given any thought to his well-being. He was very cold and very miserable and looked ill. April Lacey, his bride-to-be, was devastated when she saw the condition he was in and the photos confirmed it. We then agreed no more stupidity on the stag nights.

April's big day was marked by further controversy as Phoebe outdid the bride. She looked absolutely stunning and gained a further regiment of admirers, but she was still looking for the permanent rich kid. I remember at the evening reception I was chatting to some people when she came and joined the group with her friend, James Porteous. He was a flash sort of lad, an estate agent who lived up to every penny he earned and at the time Phoebe had her claws into him and, of course, when she introduced him to us, she couldn't resist adding, 'He's got an E-Type Jag you know.' To which James replied sarcastically, 'No, I didn't know.'

I'll never forget when she came to introduce me to anyone, it was a simple, 'and this is so and so, and this is David he works at Pennington's; it's the big factory on the outskirts of the town', and that was that. She flounced away to her architects, solicitors and bankers without a look back at her blue-collar former admirer.

My father made me Managing Director and over the years we prospered. One of my first tasks, however, was to buy Marsdens Engineers, which was owned by Frank Payne, my old boss. When I worked there I could see the potential of the firm and after taking over at Pennington's, I saw the benefits of bringing the two firms together would be enormous.

Frank wanted to retire in any event and was glad of our offer, particularly as we paid him as a consultant for many years after.

'There's many a good tune played on an old fiddle,' my father used to say, and he was right. These older more practically experienced engineers could often sort out the most difficult problems and did so saving more than I paid them in salary each year. Not only that, but they enjoyed doing it; it kept them alive. Oh god I wish I could do that now.

I developed several new projects and the firm prospered so much that we went public and both of us made a small fortune in the process. In fact, the share placing valued Pennington's at a hundred million pounds and as we retained seventy per cent of the company, our share was seventy million, which was a large fortune in anybody's book.

The *Financial Times* made a meal of the story and so did several of the other national newspapers; so much so that I remember becoming a bit of a celebrity in local circles. My father was always a fair man and invited John Pennington to join the board in a non-executive capacity and gifted him with one per cent of the company. He also put ten per cent of the shares into trust for the workforce who were still employed, together with those who had retired and benefited by over fifty thousand a year; but the important thing was it made them feel part of the firm.

We actually received over twenty-five million pounds for thirty per cent of the company, which caused a big stir locally and must had entered the ears of Phoebe.

I still had my job, a fantastic salary, a profit-sharing bonus, and I never looked back. I had all the trappings of wealth with the exception of a wife, but there I had plenty of opportunities.

Several other members of the group had tied the knot but our Phoebe was still searching for her Mr Right and . . . Dammit! I can't remember which one it was. Aaarh! Yes, it was when Clayton got married and once again Phoebe was done up to the nines. You couldn't take it away from her, she did scrub up well and was blessed with good looks and once again had an entourage of men wanting to be with her; although this group was becoming smaller and smaller as more of us drifted into marriage.

Chapter 2

It must have been Friday the thirteenth, because Phoebe came over to me on the pretext of being bothered and quite simply asked if I would take her home.

'Don't be silly, tell them you are with me and I'll take you home later. The night's too young to leave now.'

'Ooooh, David, thanks, you are a dear,' she said kissing me on the cheek.

That little sentence 'you are a dear' should have been 'I am expensive' because that's what it turned out to be, didn't it?

She clung to me like glue that evening and although I enjoyed the attention she gave me, it was the beginning of my downfall. I'd had far too much to drink to drive. No, I remember I wasn't drunk, I just felt I wasn't safe to drive. So we took a taxi and of course it was her place first.

'Come on in, David. Have a quick cup of coffee for saving my life.'

Like a dog after a bitch on heat, I alighted from the taxi and was led by the nose into her apartment. I'd had it; I was in and the door was locked. She poured me a very large brandy

'Drink this while I make the coffee.'

I didn't have time to drink it all before she was back with the coffee and sat on the arm of the settee next to me.

'Thank you for looking after me tonight. I really do appreciate it, David,' she said, whispering in my ear.

I turned to respond and she kissed me and, with the effects of the drink and having a beautiful woman seducing me, I was lost. When I look back, I thought I was a man of the world at the time, but she made me look like a raw amateur. Her kisses were full of passion as she rolled over on top of me, caressing every part of my body.

'Undo my zip,' she whispered, twisting round to make it easier. 'Come on, quick. I want you *now*.'

As I pulled down the zip, she wriggled out of her dress all in one movement, kicking it on to the floor. She wrapped herself around me, exciting me with little bites as she pushed her firm breasts into my face. She began undoing my shirt and then my trousers, never stopping her caressing. I grabbed her tightly, pulling her closer and closer as she made me want her. Suddenly, I was in her. She was sitting on top of me, screaming with delight as she maneuvered her curves in every direction. She was pushing deeper and deeper until she cried out her satisfaction, turning us over in the process as I continued to reach my own orgasm.

'Wow,' I whispered breathlessly.

'My, David, we are a big boy, aren't we?' she sighed, as we lay there breathless.

'Come on. Come with me.' She stood up and looked sensational in her underwear, holding her hand out to lead me to somewhere more comfortable. I followed, watching her naturally swaying hips, wrapped in a pair of white lacy French knickers, as she led me into the bedroom where we began again . . . and again and again.

I stayed overnight, too exhausted to move anywhere. She had really played her part well, as without doubt no man could have refused her. When I look back I don't think she would have refused any man, unless they didn't have much in the way of cash. But as a young man it was sheer, unadulterated sexual delight.

I woke up about midday to see her already in her dressing gown; she had obviously been up for some time as she was fully made-up and looked stunning.

'Tea or coffee?' she asked.

'My, waitress service as well. I am being treated well.'

'You deserve it for what you did for me yesterday.'

I thought she was talking about how I'd looked after her at the wedding.

'Any decent bloke would look after you.'

'No darling, you are a fantastic lover. I could eat you all over again.' She allowed her dressing gown to drop to the floor, revealing her beautiful body, which was being caressed by another enticing set of underwear.

'You do want me don't you?'

Jesus I didn't, but I did, I just couldn't put her down. There was no love, just sheer naked desire. It was simply fiery lust as we spent the next hour entangled on the bed. She certainly knew how to satisfy me. It was almost two o'clock in the afternoon when she said, 'Come on. I'm going to treat you to a late lunch as a thank you and we can go and pick your car up.

Well, it was my fault we ended up at the Piggot Arms, I suppose, as I let her choose where we went. She knew many of her friends would be there and of course I was the centre of attraction as it had not long been announced about the share issue in Pennington's.

'This is David. I'm treating him to lunch as he saved my life last night. Rescued me in fact. My hero, aren't you, David?'

I just grinned and I was enrolled into the little circle before I knew it, even though it was something I had never really wanted. One of the chaps had just bought a Mercedes sports car and was bragging about what it could do, how fast it could accelerate and so on, and then he asked, 'What do you run, David?'

'Oh I have a lovely little MGTC 1949; as good as new. It runs beautifully.'

Phoebe had to make sure he knew I didn't have to ride around in an old banger so added, 'David loves to use his little old car, I think he's a bit eccentric you know.'

I have never put on a show for anyone. I have never believed in trying to be better than my neighbours and I think this was the only time I felt sorry for Phoebe, when she was trying to impress this idiot. I heard him remark that she must be desperate and he even laughed that she would be using the bus next. It was quite amusing to hear his friend telling him I had just made thirty million on a deal and I very sarcastically leaned over and said, 'It was only twenty five, but never mind.'

I have never done that since and I wouldn't have then, but I just felt they had a cheek to talk about us in that way; they deserved to be put in their place and they were, because there were red faces all round.

'What was that all about?' Phoebe asked.

'Nothing, just two silly men trying to be something they are not.' I replied, hoping they would hear, but it fell on deaf ears.

I couldn't let her pay for the meal because it wasn't my style, but it was also my mistake. I should have let her pay her share, then maybe it would have been all over. But no! Because I had bought the meal, and not given her the opportunity to pay me back, she had to invite me to her apartment, she told me, where she would cook a meal for me the following Friday.

She played it very cool, making no effort to contact me, not even to confirm whether or not I would be there; but having said yes I felt I could not back out.

I rang the doorbell holding a lovely bottle of champagne and a bunch of flowers to be greeted by a beautiful woman. When I look back it was a pity the inside of her was not as lovely as the outside of her.

She looked ravishing, even with her apron on, which she removed quickly to reveal another stunning outfit.

'Ooooh, champagne, my favourite. And what beautiful flowers, thank you so much. Let me thank you properly,' she said, putting the gifts on the hall table and then grabbing me round the neck and giving me a long, passionate kiss.

'I love champagne; come on let's open it now.' She led me into the dining room where the table was set out for six.

'I hope you don't mind, I've invited a couple of friends over. I was sure you wouldn't want to be lumbered with just me for the entire evening.'

I was disappointed as I did of course want to be alone with her; but she was clever and would not let me get near her that night. She made it even worse for me by her behaviour, always touching, teasing, tempting and insinuating what I was missing. It wasn't a bad evening, the conversation was good, she had put on a lovely meal and she looked fabulous. In fact I couldn't take my eyes off her as she slinked like a cat around the room. She would catch me looking at her, my eyes full of desire, and smile at me. I really did want to go to bed with her there and then,

Her friends left at about one o'clock in the morning and after another drink I couldn't take any more teasing and decided to go too. Phoebe went to the hall, collected my coat and escorted me to the door.

'Thank you for a lovely evening,' I said trying to be polite. 'No doubt I will see you again soon.'

'I hope so,' she said. 'I've bought tickets for the opera next Friday and I'd love you to come with me. And I want some more of this,' she said, undoing the zip of my trousers and putting her hand inside.

I had been so pent up all evening that I just grabbed her and kissed her deeply and after only two or three minutes of her fondling, it was all over for me.

'Naughty, naughty,' she teased. 'I wanted you to save it for me until next weekend. You will come won't you?' she asked, still fondling me, draining me of all my common sense.

'Oh yes,' I replied breathlessly.

'Next weekend you can run it all down my body and we can

rub it in to each other. I will make it something you will never forget.'

I left her apartment with my head in the clouds. I couldn't think straight. I wanted her so badly I didn't know how I could wait until the following weekend.

All the next week, for the first time ever, I couldn't keep my mind on my work, let alone think of anything else. I remember feeling so stupid that I couldn't play it cool like her; she had me hooked. However, I had no intention of having anything other than a bloody good time, and I thought that was all she wanted too. I now realise it was her making the decisions all along. I wasn't in control of anything.

I tried to act as though she wasn't important, but that only lasted until the Tuesday, when I phoned her, but there was no reply. Nor did she answer on the Wednesday or the Thursday. Each time I left a message, but she didn't reply until the Friday to confirm the arrangements.

Unfortunately my little car was waiting for a part, so I had to use the company's Rolls-Royce, the Silver Seraph; it was the first of three we purchased and I loved them, not for their show-off appeal, but for their sheer mechanical excellence. We did all our own repairs and maintenance, stripping them down many times in our effort to copy certain things, as our engineers were equally as good as those working at Rolls-Royce Crewe.

Anyway, where was I? God I've forgotten . . . Rolls Royce Cr . . . aaah yes, I had to take Phoebe to the opera in the Seraph. I knocked on her front door and when she opened it she looked like a goddess in a long green, off-the-shoulder dress. She looked simply stunning. I can picture her now; she would have graced any magazine. Well, when she saw the car she was delighted. Mind you, she pretended that she didn't know I was wealthy and behaved as if she was very surprised.

21

I opened the door for her and then walked round to the driver's side. She leaned over as I got in, whispering, 'I hope you haven't forgotten what you promised me tonight.'

Well, that did it again, especially when she started to rub the inside of my leg. I stopped the car and leaned over to kiss her.

'No, no, don't do that, you'll spoil my make-up. Just be patient and I'll let you lick it all off when we get back home.'

I like some opera but I didn't hear much of this one. I was simply staring at Phoebe all the time and thinking how lovely she looked. I heard one of her friends sitting near us comment, 'I think he's got it bad, look at him.'

After a few drinks with her friends in the bar when the opera ended, we walked to the car. I remember that as I put my arm around her I could feel her body almost quivering with antici-pation. That's the only way I know how to describe it; it made me want to stop there and then, wherever we were, and take her.

On the journey home she would not leave me alone and the moment we entered the flat she pulled me along to the bedroom and it was a race as to who could be naked first. She made me feel like a stallion and was over me like a rash, never stopping for one minute, until, I heard that 'I am satisfied' scream as she reached the first of her many climaxes.

She was bloody good in bed and once again I stayed the night, with the same routine the following morning, only this time, when my brain was firmly stuck in my genitals, she asked me if I loved her. 'What do you think,' I replied, as I too was reaching my climax; kissing her, hugging her tightly to me and not wanting to let go.

I lay there exhausted as she caressed and relaxed me, enticing me into her web. 'Kiss me,' she whispered.

I leaned over and kissed her. I suppose at that moment I felt something for her and kissed her with a feeling to which she responded.

'Would you like to see me on Wednesday?' I asked.

'I'd love to,' she said and kissed me again, with that intense feeling she put into all the moments we had then. This time I responded and felt there might be something meaningful there.

Wednesday's date was the start of our regular dating and I began to see her three or four times a week.

James began to warn me about Phoebe, telling me to be careful, and like a fool I told him that she was bloody good in bed, to which he replied, like some old wise man, 'Bed and sex are less than ten per cent of being married.'

We had several months of excitement before she began to spoil things for me. I remember she only wanted to go out in the Seraph. She would talk about what *we* had got and yet we were not a 'we' then. Soon she started to talk about us getting together, getting engaged and so on. This kind of commitment was far from my mind, but she knew how to manipulate me with all her womanly ways and before I knew it, she had persuaded me to get engaged.

The moment we decided, I felt it was essential that I took her to meet my parents. It showed me for the first time what she was really like. We hadn't been with my parents more than fifteen minutes when she started to tell them quite categorically what she would change about me, where we would live and how I would have to behave, and whilst she was in their home, she priced everything up and even asked for one or two items as engagement presents, remarking 'You won't use these much now at your age.'

I felt dreadful and was dumbfounded at her arrogance and wanted to call it off there and then, but another wonderful weekend in bed brought me back on board.

My dad was furious and asked me if she was good in bed because that's all she would be. He told me my brains were between my legs and he was right.

I had to go to London to choose the ring as I knew a lovely little Jewish man who ran a small business called Gemstones in Hatton Garden.

I will never forget that day as long as my brain has anything left. We caught the 7.05 a.m. train from Leeds to Kings Cross, reserving seats in the restaurant for breakfast. I always loved breakfast on that train and it made the journey seem quicker.

We made our way to the seats carrying *The Times*, *Telegraph* and *Yorkshire Post* whilst Phoebe had one of the new celebrity magazines. I was a little embarrassed as she was talking somewhat loudly and would suddenly burst out laughing and point out some ridiculous dress one or another of the so-called celebrities was wearing, or tell me that so and so was getting engaged. To this, she'd look at me and add, 'I wonder if they are going to Hatton Garden for their ring, darling,' in a voice loud enough to be sure the other passengers heard.

We were halfway to London when she tired of her magazine and took the *Yorkshire Post*. I think that's the only one she would have understood. No, I'm being catty, she was educationally bright.

'Darling! We're in the paper. You didn't tell me.'

'I didn't know until I read it myself a few minutes ago, and keep your voice down, please. You're disturbing people.'

'Oh sorry,' she said turning round to acknowledge someone who had obviously been listening.

'And you didn't tell me we had won a twenty-five million pound order from Rolls—'

I stopped her in mid-sentence, putting my finger across her lips. 'Ssssh. We don't want to talk about it.'

'That's a huge order isn't it?' she asked now, whispering loudly.

'Yes it is, now change the subject.' But she couldn't.

'It calls you a tycoon darling,' she said, her voice becoming louder by the word, 'and it says you are in the top five of the Yorkshire rich list,'

'Darling, please keep your voice down and don't believe everything you read in the newspapers, particularly the *Yorkshire Post*.'

She must have read that article a dozen times, especially the bit that put me in the Rich List and by the end of the journey I think everyone on the train knew about me.

It would be unfair to say Phoebe was dressed up to the nines, as she was always smart and wore simple but elegant outfits. She could make a simple dress look stunning, as good-looking women often do. But things changed once she had money and began to wear those ridiculous designer clothes.

Now, where was I? On the train. No, think man.

Well, it doesn't matter if I don't get all the details. We arrived at Kings Cross at 10.15 a.m. and walked along the platform, followed by a barrage of eyes, just looking at a woman who was without doubt very beautiful. She linked my arm knowing that nearly every man was looking at her and walked out of the station like some goddess.

We were not expected at the jeweller's until after lunch, so first stop Oxford Street, Regent Street and then to Harrods.

I had my first glimpse of what she would become as we spent a fortune. She would not accept my advice on anything and bought things just because they were the most expensive.

We arrived at Hatton Garden and walked into the shop; you would have thought we were the richest people in the world the way she behaved and it was a good hour of this before I persuaded her to have a beautiful three-stone diamond ring. It cost eight and a half thousand pounds, bloody expensive, and even then I detected it wouldn't be good enough for her. It was beautiful, but the size was too small and had to be enlarged. It was to be ready in seven days.

'Shall I send it to you?' Isaac asked.

'No, no,' Phoebe said quickly, 'I'll come and collect it. I'd love another trip to London.'

I told her that I wouldn't have the time to go with her, but that didn't seem to matter; she was determined to do things her own way.

I had one major surprise left for her; I had booked us into the Savoy for the night. I had organised for a suitcase with the sexiest of nightwear plus a change of clothing to be sent to the Savoy in advance and, of course, I had booked tickets for a show, taking the best seats in the house.

Like any young woman she was excited by it all, but when I ordered the taxi to take us to the Savoy I could sense her apprehension. I had stayed at the Savoy regularly on business and was quite well known there.

'Good morning, Mr. Stephens,' the receptionist said the moment we walked to the desk, which impressed our little Phoebe. 'Here's the key to your room, sir. Please let me know if there is anything you need.'

'I will thank you.'

We took the lift to the second floor and made our way to our room. Two hundred and something, I can't remember which, but I can remember her reaction as she walked in and screamed with delight and even more so when she saw the contents of the case.

'Come here, you lovely man,' she said, kicking off her four-inch high-heeled shoes and then pretending she couldn't undo her dress. She took my hand and placed it on the zip and I gently pulled it all the way down to her bottom. The dress slithered over her curves until it dropped to the floor revealing her wonderful underwear, so simple yet tantalising.

I can't believe I'm remembering this, I hate the woman, but at the time I found her exhilarating, sensuous and exciting and I wanted to make love to her as often as I could.

She pulled me on to the bed, almost ripping my clothes off as she did it. 'You are a wonderful man and you deserve something special,' she said, and by god it was special, the first, second and third time. I was just glad that the room was soundproofed otherwise I'm sure her screams would have been heard in Clapham.

We slept for a good hour afterwards, only to be woken by reception asking me when I would like my taxi to the theatre. We had an hour to get ready for the show and for me this was better than a show itself. It was a dress tease, not a striptease; it was wonderfully sexy the way her clothes covered her body, and I had chosen the dress she was to wear well; again, something simple but stunning.

She was in her element at the theatre, enjoying being in the box and looking down at the many eyes looking up to see if we really were somebody well known.

We had a late meal back at the Savoy, but an enjoyable one as by this time, I remember, I was starving. But afterwards, I was too tired for anything else and fell asleep until ten the following morning.

Phoebe always seemed to be wide awake already whenever I woke up, and was actually dressed and been downstairs for the papers, which she was scouring through avidly. I pretended not to watch her but saw her look at something in it and then put it down again.

A few minutes later I stirred loudly enough for her to hear, which encouraged her to come across to the bed. 'I thought I'd let you sleep. You were dead tired last night.'

My dad was right; my brains were in my trousers as I found her irresistible, especially as her hand was in the bed and touching me before I could say anything.

'Where's my big boy this morning then?' she asked.

'Come on, you cheeky little thing. Let's go and get some breakfast,'

'No, let's have it here,' she said, leaning over to kiss me.

I love full English, but I had never eaten breakfast that way before.

There was a knock on the door and the breakfast was wheeled in. Phoebe gave the housemaid a ten-pound tip and when she'd gone, slipped out of her dress, once again revealing that lovely body bedecked in beautiful soft silk and lace, She began by cutting up my eggs and bacon and gently feeding me. Then suddenly she placed a large piece of egg between her teeth and put it to my mouth, pushing it in with her tongue. Well, that was that, my face and her body was covered with my breakfast and to this day I don't know how she managed to take her underwear off whilst we were at it.

I had to have a bath and I just couldn't bear to think what the hotel would say about the state of the bed, or the bathroom, as she also attacked me in the bath.

I was worn out before the day started and then she said, 'That was just the starter. I haven't finished with you yet. Just wait till I get you home. I told you I would thank you properly.'

We wandered round the shops, with her spending and me paying, as I wasn't fit for anything else, and then we caught a late train back home. I had brought the papers with me and began to read them, I suppose for something to do whilst we were waiting for dinner. I didn't bother to look at the *Yorkshire Post*, I left that for her. I was reading my own papers when she suddenly exclaimed, 'Look at this! How on earth did they find out about us?'

I was angry, I wanted to keep it a private affair, but obviously she didn't. I knew she had phoned the paper and was very upset. In fact, it took the edge of the entire trip and she could sense it.

'What's the matter, David?' she asked.

'I'm cross. I didn't want this publicity. If I could find out who did it, I would . . . Oh it doesn't matter.'

'Never mind, I'll soon make you forget it.'

I think she thought that would be the answer to everything, and unfortunately at the time it was, but for the rest of that day I felt somewhat miserable. I would have loved to have told her that I thought it was her who had told the newspaper about us, but I hadn't the courage.

I was cross for several days and could not hide my feelings and I could see for the first time that she was concerned that I had cooled off. Anyway, she invited me to dinner and I picked her up in the Seraph and took her to the Angel where she had arranged to go. Of course, she had to go where she knew some of her cronies would be and we had to listen to their congratulations and have a few drinks with these Hooray Henrys. By the end, if anyone else had asked when the happy day was, I would have hit them, male or female. Once again, it put a damper on the evening, especially as she was telling them how much the ring cost, whispering the price, and even adding a bit.

It was not a bad meal and for once I didn't have to pay and we were given an ice-cold bottle of Mumm to take home with us.

I remember we pulled up not far from her apartment in a lovely secluded spot and I took out the glasses from the back of the car, almost standard equipment in the Rolls, popped the cork of this delicious bottle of champagne and we drank it.

I always did love champagne as it has a wonderful effect on me. I'd forget my troubles and cares quickly and could just enjoy myself.

'You haven't had a good time, have you?' she asked.

'Of course I have. It was lovely.'

'Come here, give me a kiss.'

It was those damn kisses that always seemed to cause me trouble and within seconds she was down to her underwear and afterwards I never looked at a Rolls-Royce in the same way again.

It was fabulous, no one would believe how good she was, and again when I took her home for another bottle of bubbly and a full night of passion, it was just sensational and once again I was under her spell.

It was the following Thursday when she went down to London to collect the ring, and telephoned me to say she had a surprise for me, that things began to change me forever. She arrived back at Leeds late evening armed with bags full of goodies – new dresses, scarves and underwear – dropping them all to make a grand show of putting her arms around my neck and kissing me.

I picked up the parcels and squeezed them into the back of the MG. I could tell she was annoyed I had that car rather than the Rolls.

'Stop the car a minute I want to show you something,' she said.

I pulled over and she held out her hand to reveal a huge solitaire diamond in a setting that made it look even bigger. 'Well, what do you think?'

'It's a bit gaudy and ostentatious, where did you get it?'

'I love it. When I saw it, I had to have it and exchanged it for the other one.'

'What did you do that for? We chose the other one together.'

'I thought you would like it and it's a much better diamond. I had to put another three thousand pounds to it. You do like it, don't you?'

I didn't answer and continued the journey in silence. I had arranged to stay at her apartment, but the spirit had been knocked out of me and I went home instead.

The following day she called several times at the office only this time I was the one who didn't answer and when I got home she was waiting outside for me.

'Hello, darling, am I forgiven? Is your naughty little pussy cat forgiven? Come back to my place and I will treat you to something special.'

I did go back with her, but even the champagne could not set the world alight and I saw her for what she really was.

Chapter 3

After I foolishly got engaged, Phoebe had to have the grand party, with as many people there as the place would hold and a few outside. We hired the rugby team's social club for the do, which turned out to be a very extravagant affair, as engagement parties go. All the hangers on, well most of them, were just there for the free bar, and Phoebe was generous with that. I was glad in some ways that my parents didn't come, although her parents did and even here James told me to be careful.

The party for me was a wonderful affair; I had a whale of a time and I think if I had known before what other opportunities I had with women, I would never have got engaged. In fact, I actually had so much attention it made Phoebe jealous. I danced every dance with a different woman, including Constance Redpath, who is my one and only real love, but then it was the first time I had seen her, and she was with her husband. I must admit when I look back, as that is all I can do now, I remember that dance, a slow waltz which seemed to go on forever. I remember catching her eye several times over the evening, but of course I had to put it out of my mind.

Phoebe looked stunning as only she could and when we had the first dance to start the evening off everyone cheered and all her friends had to comment, 'You do look a lovely couple.' One had the cheek to say in an almost breathless Marilyn Monroe voice, 'David, you can tell she's in love with you; just look at the way she looks at you,'

I thought that was sheer bullshit, as I now felt it was only the pounds, shillings and pence Phoebe was really interested in.

I kept saying to myself that an engagement was not a marriage and I could string it out and still have the sex bit for a while. After the engagement party, I didn't mention the word marriage for over a year.

Phoebe began to realise I was cooling off and tried to rekindle the good old days, but it didn't work. Yes, I remember that we had sex, but there was no fiery passion in either of us. It now almost seemed like a duty with her. I actually felt there was someone else but I guess she would not risk losing the money I could give her, so she stayed with me. Anyway, we drifted along for a couple of years and every day I felt her materialism coming to the fore, and I was now totally convinced she had had her claws in me from the start just to get my money. What was so dreadful from my point of view was that the youthful desire I had felt for Phoebe had long gone. She was still very beautiful but I no longer had any real feelings for her whatsoever. It was sheer stupidity to go ahead and marry her and a recipe for disaster. She made the running and I seemed to just drift along. Her friends would always comment that we looked a lovely couple and didn't we think it was about time we got hitched, or ask when the happy day was. Phoebe loved it and would grab my arm, smile at them and then me, as though she was being coy and would answer, 'We haven't decided yet.' It made me shudder.

No, we hadn't decided, at least I hadn't decided, and I'm sure she could sense that I no longer wanted to get married, at least not to her, but somehow I found myself agreeing to a date.

She allowed me to choose the house, but I didn't have a look-in with everything else, and of course she would comment that so and so had this or that, so we had to have something different or better. Then, of course, she realised that playing bridge had become popular and decided that we should play too. I couldn't stand the game but went along for a quiet life and that's when it started: I gave in to everything for a quiet life and let her do all the running.

The items we bought for our new house were sheer opulence, I could never use them for fear of breaking them; I just wanted things to be ordinary. I look back now and realise I was weak-willed. I should have laid down some of the ground rules from the start.

My father could see through her, hence the reason for the prenuptial agreement, mainly to protect the share capital and the family interest, especially after Phoebe had said if the business was hers, she would get rid of it and spend the money. To a man who had spent his life building it up and protecting its employees, it was like a red rag to a bull.

I know she hated this agreement, but the terms she was offered were sensational as it gave her a phenomenal personal income, so she accepted immediately. We hadn't even set a date for the wedding at the time, but I think the lure of the money changed everything. It had become too much of a temptation for her to resist, so it wasn't a surprise that she became pregnant, or was it? She had always told me she was on the pill. But now I think it was an insurance that I wouldn't back off, as she could sense my change of attitude and that could spoil the opportunity for her.

I remember her telling me as though it was something magnificent. 'Darling, I've got some wonderful news, we're going to have a baby.' *We* are going to have a baby, not *I'm* going to have a baby. I felt it was said in that way to emphasise that we'd done it together and so we must now get married as soon as possible.

She was nine weeks pregnant and could have taken pills, even in those days, to end the pregnancy, but no she waited until it was too late before she told me and there was no turning back.

Four weeks later, the big day arrived. I wanted simple things, just a quiet wedding and some real friends, she wanted the lot. I remember I lost, as usual. I think if Westminster Abbey had been available to us, we would have had to have that. It wasn't the money it was the sheer waste of inviting people I had never met before and was unlikely to ever meet again. The only thing which I got my own way on was I refused to wear top hat and tails. I simply said if you don't like it you know what you can do, and I won. I should have been like that about other things, but I wasn't and I suffered for it.

I arrived at the packed church with my best man, James Percival, who later became our local doctor. I was full of trepidation and only he knew I didn't want to go through with it. I also told him she was pregnant and that I felt trapped. With a very reluctant 'I do' from me and a smile that would have cracked a mirror from her, it was all over. Over? Oh god no; it was just the beginning.

Three to four hundred guests were served in a marquee on the lawn, which made it a very grand affair that her parents couldn't afford, so my father paid. In fact, he paid for everything, but you would have thought her parents had by the way she behaved. She looked stunning as usual, and you couldn't tell she was pregnant. Even the local press made a feature of her in her gown. I did get a mention as well, however only that I was the MD of Pennington's.

I had no sexual relationship whatsoever with Phoebe after the marriage, hardly even a kiss. She said was pregnant and didn't want to risk the child. In fact, there was no warmth from her at all, but I put up with it thinking it was simply because she was pregnant.

She spent her time getting her feet under the table and laying down the law on what should be done in the house by all the staff. Then, she turned her attention to Pennington's for the first time.

She walked into the offices as though she owned the place and began dictating that someone should pick up the rubbish that was lying around or that in the men's toilet the light had been left on.

Of course, it was only a few minutes later that I received a phone call from the shop steward asking if I would keep her away as her attitude was upsetting everybody and, what's more, it was a gents toilet and if a woman was going to walk in, a sign should be put up to warn the men.

I'll never forget one of the shop stewards telling me politely that I should not allow her into the factory, and should not let her speak to the employees in the way she did.

'I'll try George,' I said, 'but you know what she's like. Its nigh on impossible.'

'We might teach her a lesson next time.'

'Do that, you've got my blessing.'

I had a quiet word with her, but she stormed into a rage.

'Who the bloody hell do these people think they are. I pay their wages for god's sake. Don't they realise that?'

'Well actually, Phoebe, *you* don't Pennington's does.'

'But we own Pennington's'

It was no use; I had to let it go.

When our firstborn arrived seven months later, I knew she had got me one way or the other; I could never leave her now. She tried to pretend to everyone the baby was two months premature and I let her pretend. Our other children came in quick succession and by the sixth year of marriage, shortly after my thirty fifth birthday, we were having our fourth child. After three boys, Josh, Simon and William, we had a little girl, Hannah. But after each child, the delectable Phoebe became more and more materialistic. We had two nannies as she felt with all our money she should not have to do housework and that bringing up four children was housework. We had to have a live-in housekeeper, Mrs Cripp, who became my only ally in the house. Phoebe always had to have the best and yet she never learned that the most expensive was not always the best. Oh and those silly fashions she wore, and still does, designed by some big name. She had to have them regardless of whether or not they made her look ridiculous, and they often did.

This was not my style. I hated the pretence and I hated trying to be better than my neighbours and friends, but the problem was it seemed that all our new friends were really Phoebe's and they were all of similar ilk, which made home life impossible for me. I stayed at the office more and more, just to be out of the way. This also turned out to be a disaster as the more work I did, the more successful I became, and the more money I made. Which in turn meant the bitch spent more; it was self-perpetuating. I began to hate going to work. Why should I be missing out on the normal things in life? Oh, I wished that I had done things differently.

When Josh was four he was packed off to boarding school and so were the others, including Hannah, the moment the schools would take them; there was no way small children were going to ruin the life Phoebe wanted to lead. However, they still had to have everything, if not more, than all the other kids: the best tricycles, the best bicycles, ponies. What was so stupid, whilst they were at school the ponies were in livery at an enormous cost to me, and hardly ever ridden. I didn't dare say anything though or we would have tantrums for days, and I often said whatever was needed to get peace and quiet.

The children all did reasonably well at school and I remember I went to a parents' day on my own once to talk about how each of the boys was doing, and one of the form masters asked, 'Is your wife here today?' I couldn't believe the words that came out of my mouth, but I replied, 'Oh no, she's done her bit by having them.' The form master gave an embarrassed half laugh, half choke, and nothing more was said.

The boys never came to me if they wanted anything, it was always to their mother they went to as they only had to ask, knowing she would never question their requests. They were three very spoilt boys. It was only when Josh became seventeen that I put my foot down about a car. I told him and the others they would have to pass their test before I would consider thinking about it.

'Don't worry, darling,' Phoebe commented, 'you will have your car' After that comment, I put my foot down for the second time.

'I'll decide whether or not we will buy him a car. In fact, he should damn well work for it,'

She didn't speak to me for a week.

The following week, still sulking, she suddenly announced, 'I've got my own money. I'll buy him a car myself.' She stamped her foot and just stormed off, and I was able to enjoy another week of quiet bliss.

Hannah was the only one who really excelled at school and the only one who was remotely interested in what I did for a living. In fact, it was me who discouraged her in the beginning as I thought engineering was for men. But as she progressed I could tell she had an aptitude for it and so from then on I encouraged her.

She was my only ally, excluding my parents that is. I remember when she was still a little girl and I was away on business, I telephoned to see how she was; we were in the middle of our conversation when suddenly Phoebe started interrupting. Nasty comments seemed to fall from her lips like rain and, once started, it was hard for her to stop.

'Dad, do you mind if I talk to Mum for a minute?'

'No. Not at all.'

'Mum, please don't be rude to Dad. Right, Dad, where were we?' And she was only just four years old.

I know it was my own fault with the children, I never seemed to find time to be with them, or was it solely I couldn't bear to be near Phoebe, I can't remember, but of course I dutifully supported them at school with all their activities and then on to university and into their careers, but it really wasn't enough. I was closest to Hannah as we had more in common. She was more business minded and wanted to join the firm, which I was not happy with, but at the time left things open until she had gained her degree and had experience with other organisations.

So, I suppose I deserve all I get now, but I did decide I wanted to know my grandchildren as and when they arrived, and I have benefited from this because I know they love me and I do love to see them, especially now.

Phoebe and I went our different ways: she had her committees and her social activities; the coffee mornings, the tea afternoons and at least once a week a dinner engagement, which I was supposed to attend and usually did. I simply had my work. We had no sexual relationship after about eight years. I could not pretend otherwise, but Phoebe could and would put on a show of affection in front of others.

I decided it would be better if we could get away for a few weeks each year or have the odd long weekend away, so I bought a plot of land next to a French friend of mine and built a lovely house in a little village called La Croix Valmer in the Var, Cote d'Azur.

We went there several years running for our holidays with the children but although they were very enjoyable, the house was not grand enough for Phoebe, even though we had a daily housekeeper and she really didn't have to do a lot. Eventually she decided she wouldn't go there anymore, but this turned out to be a blessing in disguise as I continued spending several weeks a year there on my own, fishing and socialising with the neighbours. They stopped asking about the family after a couple of years or so.

I love to think about the times I spent in La Croix Valmer, which unlike many of the small towns in the area had not been allowed to over-develop. There are no tall apartment blocks in areas where the view would be spoiled, and this ensures the properties themselves retain any view they had when constructed. The village is typical of those in Provence, very simple in layout;, the buildings displaying an array of pastel colours which contrast beautifully with the many flower beds provided by the local council and which are full of colour all year round. It has a wonderful microclimate as it is surrounded by the sea on its south side, with wonderful beaches, and on all the other sides it is sheltered by mountains.

During the winter these mountains are covered in mimosa, creating a huge yellow backcloth to the village, and during the summer we see the hundreds of massive 'pin parasol' pine trees which look like huge green umbrellas and keep everything underneath them cool, the perfect place for the picnic. Its only downfall is in July and August when the population increases from five thousand to fifty thousand and it is too damned hot.

When I look back we had a busy social life, but it really was all Phoebe's. She adored bridge and I would be dragged along to make up a four or simply to act as steward, especially if it was at our house. 'David you don't mind, do you? Philip's a much better player. You run along and pour us all a drink.'

I could see some of our guests wince as I went and did as I was told. None of them realised that it gave me the opportunity to sit in another room and read or have a chat with someone who could talk about things other than shopping.

We were brought together for each of the boy's weddings where Phoebe was in her element, offering to fund this and that, arranging to pay for the reception so that she could control what was done.

William was the first to tie the knot. He married a pretty little brunette, Toni Wilkes. She would not at the time say boo to a goose, and was Phoebe's ideal choice of daughter-in-law and by the time she had moulded and manipulated her, Toni was putty in her hands. The reception was a grand affair, but nothing like the one we had for Simon and his wife Pricilla. On this occasion Mr. and Mrs. Wentworth, Pricilla's parents, were very cross with the way Phoebe was taking over, but when they found out what the cost was going to be, they soon backed off. We seldom saw them after the marriage; it seemed we were not their type of people.

Josh was the oldest and the last of the boys to get married, but it was his wedding to Wendy Jones, aaah well, that was to be the biggest and the best. A wedding to beat all weddings was Phoebe's motto for this one. Wendy's parents were not well off, so Phoebe made a point of asking them if we could pay for the wedding as a present. They of course accepted and I knew nothing of it. I remember there were two hundred guests and it cost over thirty thousand pounds, which was a small fortune at the time. The extravagance caused a rift between the offspring as it was obvious who the favourite was, but the silver-tongued Phoebe managed to convince them that we were now better off than we had been when the other two sons got married.

Now there was only Hannah left at home and I felt I could indulge myself by spending more time at our house in France and at least have a break from all the stress with Phoebe.

Our Silver wedding was the biggest farce and the biggest charade ever, and what was worse, everybody knew we were no longer close and yet we or should it be she organised a magnificent spread in the garden with about a hundred invited guests. She was made up to the nines, lording it over everyone and fawning over me as though we were loves lost dream; clinging on to my arm as though she meant it.

"I'm glad I can't remember much about it; in fact I don't want to remember it."

"David are you all right you sound very cross?"

I must have said something to bring her in, well I am cross I hated my silver wedding.

"Can't you tell me?"

"I hated it."

"What?"

My silver wedding, go away please Oh I'll just ignore her. I want to remember what I was thinking about,

"Come on now settle down," the nurse said.

Where was I? I know I went to my room for most of the time. Oh that was it, I hated everything about it. In fact I cannot remember anything that endears me to Phoebe.

I suppose my real troubles started to show when I had just turned sixty. I began occasionally to forget a simple little thing. We would be going out somewhere and I would have to check whether I had locked the house, or when we left the car some-where I would have to go back to see if it was locked. I began to check twice and this began to get on Phoebe's nerves.

'For god's sake, come on. You've already done that.' Then she would scream at me: 'Come on, we're going to be late.' And when we did arrive she would then try to belittle me in front of her friends, 'He's so security conscious he has to check two or three times before he is satisfied.' I would try and laugh it off with the odd comment 'You can't be too careful these days can you?'

'David what are you laughing at? You'll disturb the entire hospital, let alone the ward.' Sister said.

'I was thinking about Phoebe when I left her at the hospital and she couldn't cope with the embarrassment.' Bloody hell! I've told her.

'Come on now; settle down, you can think about it tomorrow.'

How can I stop thinking about things? It's all I've got left.

*

41

Now where was I? Yes, that's it; I went to the hospital with Phoebe.

Yes I was really at the beginning of things as our friends also began to notice I was becoming what appeared to be more absent-minded and our so-called friends would always say I was working too hard, or I had too much on my mind and so on. Anyway, Phoebe suddenly developed a small blemish on her chin and couldn't cope with 'looking ugly'. A friend told her to go and get it removed and recommended the best specialist you could possibly get. There was no dilly-dallying with Phoebe, the moment the word 'best' was used, she immediately made arrangements to see him and within days she was booked into the Leeds General Infirmary to have the blemish removed.

Well, I remember it was a nightmare to park anywhere near the hospital and we drove round and round until she snapped. 'Oh for god's sake, drop me off and then go and find a place and come back and wait for me. I'll only be about half an hour.'

I drove back to the hospital with her constantly shouting: 'Quickly, we'll be late.' Or, 'Can't you damn well hurry up?'

Eventually we arrived at the entrance and without another word she got out of the car in an almighty huff, slamming the door in the process, much to the amusement of the passers-by, and stormed into the hospital. I then set off to find a parking space. Only I didn't; for some reason I drove home. I was pulling into the drive when the phone rang. I didn't answer but put it on loudspeaker to listen to the inevitable message.'

'Where the hell are you?' she shouted down the phone. 'Come and get me. I can't stand around like this. Don't you realise I've had an operation on my face?'

Then I remembered I should have been at the hospital. The phone rang again. 'Never bloody mind, I'll take a bloody taxi . . .' she paused, 'moron,' and cut off.

I knew I would be in trouble the moment she returned and I was right. I was hiding in the study when she thundered in.

'Look at me. I've had to walk halfway through Leeds with this on my face. Don't you realise how embarrassing that was for me? And you simply forgot? What kind of a man are you when you can do this sort of thing?'

I looked at her with the smallest little plaster on her face you could imagine; I remember thinking 'What have I married. God help me'

I had, however, began to lose a little confidence and was having to rely on *her* more and more, which she initially seemed to enjoy as she now had more power over me and was more in control. So much so that my home, if I can call it a home, was beginning to seem more like a luxury social club, particularly with members of the bridge club. They used every excuse possible to visit: there were committee meetings, extraordinary meetings, and these became the ordinary, and of course there were the matches.

I should have had a sign put on the door: 'Haworth Bridge Club meets here every Tuesday and the first Friday in the month, until the booze runs out'. They had more takers on those days than any other. Phoebe loved it.

Oh god! I'm rambling again, where the hell was I? I remember, it was during one of those evenings, when the bridge club was meeting at our house for a practice session that I was once again sent into another room out of the way, only this time I had a female companion. Constance Redpath.

'You're working too hard, David,' she said. She was the only female friend we had who had shown any care or concern for me, and she only said this when she was sure we were on our own and out of earshot.

She commented on more than one occasion that I should go and see the doctor. She always whispered it privately to me, as though I was special and that it was important to her. I had considered doing just that but she spurred me on.

I remember from that moment on, I knew I was in love with

43

her and what was worse I wanted to tell the world and didn't seem to care who knew it. I wanted to be with her for the rest of my life and I actually thought that Constance loved me.

I naturally went to see James Percival our local GP and long-time friend. We'd been at school together and grew up together, only going our separate ways at university. He went to medical school and I went to study business management and engineering. But even then, we met during the holiday periods and frequently travelled in Europe together, particularly to the South of France – for wine, women and song, as young lads do. I suppose I was lucky to have my own car, which was unusual in those days, and the MG was a real girl puller and we were never short of them. He was always the lucky one, for the moment they knew he was a doctor they were putty in his hands. As for me, when I told them I was an engineer they assumed I was blue collar and worked in a factory so he was the desirable one.

James was the best man at my wedding, even though he had tried to persuade me against getting involved with dear old Phoebe. I was best man at his wedding when he married his lovely nurse and quite honestly, I was jealous of their happiness.

We made foursomes for a short time but a simple nurse wasn't really Phoebe's cup of tea.

'Hello, David, I've been expecting you for some time. Constance told me she was worried about you and she even asked me to call at the office; but I couldn't do that.'

We chatted for a while and I explained what sort of life I was leading before I was given a thorough examination. James felt that I had been working too hard and should take it easy. 'You really do need to go away for a few weeks and rest,' he told me. However, he was somewhat concerned and suggested I visit a specialist for further tests.

It was lovely to know that Constance had cared enough to speak to James on my behalf and as a thank you I took her out to dinner. One could say it was a mistake, as it simply confirmed that I had fallen for her hook, line and sinker, and for the first time in my life, since childhood, I was happy, really happy. I don't know whether Phoebe knew or whether she was too busy to even be bothered, but I knew I wanted to be with Constance.

I remember I took her to this lovely little restaurant with lots of nooks and crannies, it felt as though we were on our own and made everything perfect that evening. I was looking at her in a way that betrayed my emotions as she suddenly leaned over and whispered, 'I think you are falling for me.'

I touched her hand, which she gently held and I whispered back to her, 'Constance, I am over sixty years old and I know I am in love for the first time in my life.'

Chapter 4

Constance had lost her husband some two years earlier to cancer and was a free agent, which enabled us to spend as much time as we could together. When James, my doctor, suggested I went away to rest for a few weeks, that was my signal to suggest we go to my house in La Croix Valmer. It was a lovely house near the centre of the village, overlooking the sea with the mountains behind it. I knew Phoebe wouldn't come and who better to spend the time with than Constance. We made no secret of it, in France that is, and I'm sure my housekeeper Simone felt the whole place was in a happier state, and she seemed to love us being there.

It was paradise. I can close my eyes and feel the sun and imagine the sea with its deep blue colour molding itself to the sky on the horizon, and then a little breeze would caress it and create thousands of sparkling diamonds as the sun touched them, before disappearing and the sea would again become still and inviting.

We had fallen in love. It wasn't just about sex. We loved each other's company. We loved to hold hands and walk where the fancy took us. Constance would give me a gentle peck on the cheek, not caring who was around, wanting to show the world she really did care for me, and I loved it. We loved walking to the market on Sunday mornings where almost everything you could think of was on sale. Then we'd move on to the boulangerie for fresh baguettes, croissants or cakes, followed by a walk to the beach, which was almost deserted as the holidaymakers had long since gone.

I remember one lovely afternoon when the hot sun had baked everywhere dry and it was just beginning to cool and Constance pulled me out of my chair.

'Come on, I'm taking you out for a walk, we've got a lot of work to do.' This meant I was to undergo more brain exercises, a daily chore that was essential to my well-being.

I couldn't resist her demands in any way and within minutes we were walking up the slope, on to the main road away from the village. The first touches of the early mimosa were just beginning to show, making a lovely contrast to the autumn leaves that had turned to deep reds and golds and had begun to fall. Constance decided that we should walk up to Les Hautes de Peynie, take the first track into the forest, and just wander. I wondered if anyone else could have been as happy as me at this moment in my life.

We were well into the forest when she suddenly stopped, put her arms around my neck, pulled her face close to mine and kissed me. I hardly remember falling to the floor with my lips still welded to hers, or the soft, gentle way we caressed each other as we made love; but I do remember that I felt I never wanted it to end and that this was the happiest day of my life. We lay in the forest looking up at the tops of the trees gently moving back and forth as if they were trying to stop the sun's rays from hitting us, but instead they were sending rippling pools of light all around us. It was truly magical.

We stayed where we were for what seemed like hours just gazing up to the sky when she suddenly asked:

'What have we been doing these last few minutes?'

'What do you mean,' I asked.

'What I say. What have we been doing these last few minutes?'

'Making love, I suppose.'

'There; you haven't lost your memory yet, or anything else. Have you? Come on, let's go,' she said, as I put my arm around her shoulders, with hers tightly gripped around my waist, and we set off walking deeper into the forest.

I could feel we were both on air and hadn't noticed the sky had darkened, or heard the distant rumbles of thunder, simply thinking they were the noise of jet planes bringing another contingent of tourists to this paradise. In fact, it was now decidedly black. Suddenly, as often happens in the mountains in the late autumn we found ourselves in the midst of a violent thunderstorm and the mountains are not the best place to be. Now, huge spots of heavy rain were percolating down through the trees and within seconds we were soaked to the skin.

The forest floor was bathed in light and the trees momentarily silhouetted as the lightning flashed overhead to the simultaneous enormous bang, as the thunder hit the side of the mountain and bounced over to the other side and back again and again. Its last rumbles slowly left the valley at the other end only to be followed by another flash of lightning and more thunder.

I covered Constance's head with my arm to protect her as much as I could, but it was impossible so we just had to grin and bear it. It was only her smiles that made it a very pleasurable occasion for me.

The storm passed as quickly as it came leaving two soaking wet forest rats to follow the stream-laden track back out to whence we came. Our slow walk had become almost a run and even our special place seemed to have become a pond.

We arrived back home decidedly different to how we had left and both of us dropped all our wet clothes in the middle of the hall and made a mad dash to the bathroom, laughing as we did so like two silly young kids experiencing the excitement of the moment of getting to know each other for the first time. We kissed and cuddled and hugged, rubbing each other to stop the cold from spoiling the occasion, until the bath was ready and we both jumped in. I wrapped my legs around her body and she rested her head on my shoulder as we sank into the lovely hot water. Not a sound was heard as we lay there in total silence and peace, my arms now underneath her breasts as she gently ran her fingers along my arms, sending soporific tingles through my body.

I remember I fell asleep and even when she said, 'Come on, darling, it's getting cold,' I didn't want to move.

I enjoyed being dried down by my Geisha girl and trying to dry her down without getting too excited. I failed miserably, which once again resulted in loving-making starting on the floor and ending on the bed.

Later we got ready to walk to Cavalaire, the nearest large town, to look at the shops and then go on to what had become our favourite restaurant 'La Mise à L'eau', for fresh gambas with aioli and a few glasses of the local rosé wine.

It was such a different relationship to what I'd had with Phoebe. Her materialism hadn't been compatible with good sexual relations. She had had her four dutiful children to cement the marriage, and that had been enough for her.

I know I'm losing my memory, but I cannot remember the last time I even slept in the same bed as her let alone had sex.

I hated her materialism, but to give her money was a cheap way of avoiding confrontation. She could never pass a shop without buying something, whether she needed it or not, and would make a fuss at the same time, never buying the cheapest of anything on principal.

Phoebe had never been interested in my welfare: as long I could go to work and bring in plenty of money she was content and now when all I have left are my thoughts, I realise she didn't want me for myself at all. She didn't want to be with me and didn't really want to have me around either. Of course, we were invited to dinner parties and other functions and even had our own, including the annual works dinner, but we never spent time together, only for the photographs or for appearances sake.

In a short time I found that Constance was the opposite. She really did love to be with me and window-shopping was simply a means of achieving that. She was interested in my welfare and worried about my memory loss, stopping me from drinking too much and spending many hours each day making me remember things that had happened during the day, and even buying various books to help with memory training. I must say things did seem to improve. Our conversations were intense; it seemed we had a lifetime to catch up with and wanted to bring it up to date as soon as we could.

The Var, Provence and the Alps Maritime have the best of everything in France and after having had such a wonderful time, neither of us wanted it to end, but end it did, especially as James had referred my case to a neurologist and the appointment date had been set for the following week.

We spent our last night in Nice taking a slow stroll along the Promenade des Anglais, letting the warm October breeze waft a few leaves that had been tempted off the trees around us. The sea only seemed to have the strength to ripple to the shore before being sucked back into the calm. It was paradise.

The two-hour flight back to England had seemed to take just a few minutes as we walked down the gangway and across to Arrivals. There was no one to meet us so it was with a long lingering kiss that we said our goodbyes, followed by many looking-backs for that last wave before we were out of each other's sight.

I remember hating going home. In all my life I had never experienced such love and affection; Constance wanted nothing more than to be in my company and when I look back, and that is now all I can do, I know that was all I really wanted out of life.

'You've decided to come back have you?' the Dragon commented as she passed me on her way to the study.

'I wouldn't have done except I have an appointment with the specialist on Tuesday.'

'What's that about then?' she asked.

'Oh, it's just a check-up.'

She didn't even bother to find out why it was necessary, instead I was treated to the usual indifference.

'I'm going over to Pat's to play bridge; I don't suppose you want to come?'

'No. I'll just relax after the journey.'

'OK. 'Bye. Don't wait up.'

Even the children didn't bother to ring although they knew I was coming home that day.

I just remember vegging out, picking up the phone and spending an hour just chatting to Constance about the wonderful five weeks we'd had.

Tuesday arrived all too quickly and I made my way to the hospital to see the specialist wondering if I had been such a terrible person that neither my wife nor any member of the family had wanted to wish me the best of luck. Not one of them had offered to be with me, if only to act as my chauffer.

My heart was racing as I waited with all the other patients, everyone looking pensive, wondering what their problem really was. All fearing I'm sure the BIG C; but I was not prepared for the results I was to get. It was the furthest thing from my mind.

I was called into the consultation room and met a lovely young man, Mr. Andrew Wilberforce. He was a top man in his field with a superb bedside manner. He was so kind and understanding, explaining fully all the tests and the purposes thereof in such a way that you were immediately relaxed and so began my examination.

I had no idea it would take so long, but Andrew, as he insisted I call him, outlined what was to happen, the first half of which would be various tests as to memory, almost like an IQ test, followed by general discussion about all aspects of my life, then questions and answers. These were to be conducted by a specialist nurse.

'Now then,' was her first opening remark, which I thought was a bit severe. 'May I call you David?'

'Yes, sure.'

'Well, we have a lot to get through and you seem an intelligent bloke, so I would be grateful if you could help me to save me calling for assistance.'

I soon learned that this was a technique to give the patient confidence, which helps to get the best out of them, particularly in the testing procedures. A more relaxed person gives a truer picture.

'The first test David is the TYM test. Any ideas of the meaning?'

'Something to do with memory?'

'Yes good. It simply means "test your memory". Look, I don't want you to feel you're wasting your time because I know you will know the answers, but I do want you to tell me. OK?'

'Yes.'

'What are these?' she asked, holding up a banana, then a torch, and finally a glass, and of course I answered correctly.

We then talked about my home life and I confessed I hadn't really got one for a few minutes and then, out of the blue, she asked me what the three objects we had looked at in the beginning had been. I'm sure it took several minutes for me to answer.

'There was a torch,' I replied, followed by a long silence, which she broke.

'Never mind, you did very well. Well done.' I felt very pleased with myself and almost shouted the words, 'And a banana and a drinking glass.'

'Oh, very well done, David, excellent.'

I was then put through the MMSE exam (the Mini Mental State Examination). This was a written test with simple questions: Date of birth. How long I'd been married – and I foolishly wrote 'too long'., the names of my children and their date of births; all very simple. Next, where I went for my holidays. Then we had the counting backwards from twenty down,

Finally, I had to copy the simple outline of two pictures – a boat and a person. I passed these tests with ninety per cent, which she announced with another 'well done'. But, as I found out, I had made a few unexpected errors. I returned to see Andrew for the next tests, which were to be various brain scans and it took some forty-five minutes before I found myself back in his consulting room for the first possible diagnosis.

'What's your prognosis?' I remember asking after Andrew, had said, 'Well, that's your lot for the time being.'

'It's too early to be sure yet, but from my experience I am really sorry to have to tell you that I think you are in the very early stages of dementia. But we have many tests to carry out and we will do these over the next few months. I shall want you to come back every three to four weeks and let me have a look at you.'

I remember sinking back in my chair, lost, heartbroken, shocked and numb all in one go.

He then started to explain that things had moved on scientifically and things weren't as bad as a few years ago. He emphasized that if it was dementia, we had caught it in the very early stages and the deterioration could be controlled to some degree, but I honestly didn't hear him. The next thing I remember was his nurse bringing me a cup of sweet tea and smiling.

'I know things are difficult at the moment but try and drink it. It'll help hot sweet tea always does' Andrew said. 'Is there anyone with you to drive you home? I don't think you are in a fit state to drive, David.'

It dawned on me for the first time what things were really like, when I replied, 'No, I haven't, they were all too busy.'

We chatted for a while until I had finished my tea and it was obvious he had to see his next patient.

'Come on, David, I'll take you to reception and they will get you a taxi. I'll see you again the same time next week. I'll do some more tests and then we can decide what treatment is best for you.'

I walked out of his surgery in a daze, but to my absolute

delight Constance was waiting in reception. I could see the pleasure in Andrew's face as he realised I had someone after all.

'Andrew, this is Constance, she is my best friend.'

I couldn't believe that I had introduced her in that way.

He smiled. 'Good, then I will leave you in her tender care.'

'I didn't think I had anybody.'

'Well, you have; you've got me, David, for as long as you want me,' Constance said as she linked my arm through hers and walked me out of the clinic.

We sat in her car for well over an hour and I just sobbed as I told her of my situation. All the time she kept saying, 'Don't worry, darling, I'll look after you.'

'You can't! It's not fair! I shall be a cabbage and I don't want to put you through this . . . I can't put you through this . . . I won't.'

She put her finger to my lips to stop me from saying anything else and then added, 'But I want to look after you. I want to be with you whatever happens.'

She put her arms around me and hugged me, slowly bringing me back to reality. She treated me to a very late lunch before taking me back to the clinic to pick up my car. I was still fit, still of sound mind and had to make plans for my future.

Chapter 5

I went home in the evening as usual and after having dinner, I was casually asked how I had got on with the doctor.

'Oh, it was just stress. I knew it would be, so there is no need to worry.'

'I wasn't,' the great Phoebe said in a really nasty way, and that was the last time anything about my health was mentioned for many months.

I spent the next few days rewriting my will and arranging where I would like to go at the end of my life, with some big caveats. I was to be fully nursed at home and if I was dumped in a nursing home at any time, then all the money due to my wife would be given equally to the various charities I had named.

I went to see my father and mother who were now themselves in the latter stages of their lives, as they were both in their early nineties, thankfully not with dementia. I was obviously not my usual self somewhat quiet which prompted both to ask what the matter was, but I couldn't tell them. I simply said I was a little tire from working too hard and needed a freak.

My dad and I discussed Pennington's and what I intended to do; he was always very supportive and suggested I moved myself upstairs and brought in a managing director to help me.

"It would help you and give you time to develop your new ideas."

I remember I began to clear my desk so to speak and gave an immediate gift of all my shares held in Pennington's, the public company, to Constance, because even though I had only known her for such a short time, I knew I wanted to spend the rest of my life with her. I left the children two hundred and fifty thousand pounds each and to Phoebe, the same, but also the house with a trust fund to manage and maintain it – unless that is, she dumped me in a nursing home. I made another immediate gift of my house in France to Constance, as a thank you for the most wonderful holiday of my life. All I had to do was survive seven years and the gifts would be substantiated and free of tax.

I decided to see James again, not only to apprise him of my thoughts, but also to make sure that he could confirm that I was of sound mind when I signed all the documents, so that the will could not be challenged. It meant I had to go through another array of tests and examinations to confirm that I was of sound mind. I had to face a panel of two neurologists, a psychiatrist, an independent lawyer, who was none other than the President of the Law Society, and a General Practitioner – though not James – and thankfully I passed with flying colours

The will was verified by all parties who confirmed it represented my true thoughts. It was then to be locked away until the day I died. The only exception was Constance. I told her what I had done. She was furious with me and said she did not want the money, or need it; all she wanted was me, warts and all.

From that moment on I decided to live what I had left of my active life to the full.

The following week I returned to see Andrew Wilberforce, the specialist, accompanied this time by my best friend, with no shame. After all, Constance was the only interested party. I even invited her in to hear what he had to say. Andrew confirmed his diagnosis, but then went on to explain that he would put me on some medication, which could possibly slow down the onset of the disease, and hopefully prolong an active life. He would see me on a regular monthly basis to begin with and from then on play it by ear.

I remember asking, 'How long have I got to be normal?'

'That's hard to say; you are undoubtedly in the very early stages, however, it could attack with a vengeance immediately or it could take years, even ten or more before you really notice a big change. But you must try to help yourself. I want you to keep your memory going and that is why I want you to go and see Dorothy Lovejoy.' Constance and I looked at each other and smiled as Andrew continued. 'She is a specialist in this field and is very, very good; she will help you to keep your brain active and that is the most important thing you can do. You must converse, you must be active, and you must not sit and feel sorry for yourself; to do so will be fatal.'

'We will do that, won't we?' Constance interrupted, before I had chance to reply.

'Yes.' I felt I could take on the world at this moment in spite of the terrible news I had just had confirmed, and when I heard Andrew whisper, 'Look after him, he needs someone like you,' I knew she would give me the courage.

I carried on working for a while, not because I had to, but I was now surprisingly enjoying my life. Constance had given me a new lease of life. I also had a few opportunities to see through, one or two of which would bring in rich rewards if I saw them to fruition.

I had one big problem though, as I appeared to be getting absent-minded and even the workforce noticed. They were actually very supportive of me from the shop floor to the management level below me, as I and my father had always been of them.

If any of them had been in trouble we were always the first to offer help; if any had run up debts we would always try and find solutions for them; or if any had health problems we would always visit to offer our help. So it was pleasing to know they were on my side. There was now always a 'good morning', 'how do you feel today?', or offers of help from one or another, but it was this absent-mindedness that was beginning to cause real difficulties and personal embarrassment, and to my cost I found that one of the staff had taken advantage of it.

The problem was compounded by the fact that the man, Vaughan Williams, was a bridge-playing friend of Phoebe's and often at our home. In fact, they had been friends for a long time.

I remember when our accountant retired and I had not long taken over the business from my father, Phoebe approached me to see if I could give Vaughan a job. I always had the belief that you should never give employment to friends as it always ends in fall-outs and tragedy. However, just to keep her off my back, as always, I offered him the job, giving him a six-month trial to see if he liked us and we liked him.

Over the next few months I remember he was always at our house playing bridge or simply visiting Phoebe. I was sure deep down he was having an affair with her. God knows why, for he was an insipid man with no real ambition, but they hit it off. He could do his job satisfactorily. I had no complaints, but that's all he would do. He wouldn't help others if they were in difficulty and was never really part of the team. The one thing that bothered me, however, was I could sense he was jealous of what we had achieved. I remember on one occasion, during one of our works meetings, he came out with the comment, 'It's all right for you. Your dad left you a big business, you don't have to worry about money do you?'

It took the shop steward to jump to my defence. 'Mr Williams, I resent that remark. You have sat on your arse for months in the office from nine till five; Mr. Stephens hasn't. I've seen him night after night working on problems after he has done his nine till five. I don't begrudge him anything.'

'Thank you, Frank—' I said, but was interrupted by Teddy Jones the transport manager, before I could finish.

'I'll second that, boss. This is the best firm to work for in the area and that's why there's a waiting list and that's why no one wants to leave. There were never finer men than him and his father.' He looked directly at Vaughan Williams as he spoke, who in turn was looking decidedly sheepish.

'He didn't mean it to sound like it did, I'm sure.' I said, springing to his defence.

'Well, he said it, and he'll have to be more careful in future, won't he?'

'Come on. I don't want this to be discussed any further, so let's move on,' I said, trying to calm things down. I did actually feel proud that the workforce in general supported me and for the things said about my father and me.

Surprisingly, Williams didn't seem at all concerned by what he had said; even the looks that he was getting from some of the others didn't seem to faze him.

Later in the day he did try to ingratiate himself by coming to discuss trivial matters but I could see through that. Never once did he apologise for his bitter outburst. I couldn't seem to get rid of him on that day as we had a visit from him in the evening, to play bridge, of course, hurriedly organised by Phoebe as a practice for their league match which was coming up.

From that day onwards I felt, no, that's not strong enough, I was *sure* Vaughan Williams was jealous of me. He could see what the company was making as he did the books, and he resented it. Yet he continued to work there. I could now feel his resentment when he was at our house. I could see him looking at anything new that Phoebe might have bought, which was often, and hear him on occasions pass a whispered comment to one of the others. The more he came and the more I saw him at work, I could see the jealousy eating into him, like some disease.

The men at work could also sense his attitude and the fact he was not a team player, and were wary of him.

Anyway, my absent-mindedness, I believe, made it easy for people to take advantage of me and it was this I think made the resentful Vaughan Williams begin to take a little for himself. Like any dishonest person, they start with a little and that becomes easy, so they increase the stakes and soon it becomes a habit.

I relied solely on the firm's accountant to keep the books properly, as I genuinely didn't have the time, and then the auditors would check the accounts at the end of the year. They had commented on the fact that there were regular small payments taken out of the account at the end of the last financial year, but as it only amounted to about eight hundred pounds I told them not to bother as it would cost more than that to investigate and it wasn't worth it.

The auditor, Joselyn de Frain, had a young trainee accountant in his office and as an exercise asked him to try and find out what had happened to the money, but after a few days he said he couldn't. Joselyn followed this up by asking for the cheque books but suddenly they had disappeared. This set alarm bells ringing that something was not right.

Joselyn came to see me and told me that he suspected that Vaughan Williams was embezzling money from the firm.

Oh god! I remember this. I had to tell Phoebe I thought her friend was stealing from us and she wouldn't have it.

'Vaughan is one of my best friends,' she snapped. 'He wouldn't do such a thing. Anyway how much is it?'

'I don't know, but they are suspicious about a missing eight hundred pounds.'

She laughed her head off in her supercilious way. 'I could spend that on a dress, for god's sake. Do you think he would do this for the cost of a dress? Oh grow up, David,' she said and flounced away.

However, Joselyn recommended that he conduct a proper investigation into the accounts and it wasn't long before they discovered that from the first few weeks of the New Year, over ten thousand pounds had gone adrift.

I had to talk the matter over with Phoebe again.

'It's a witch-hunt, a bloody witch-hunt and it's only because he's a friend of mine that you are doing it.'

'Phoebe, it's not. The auditors have discovered this and they believe it is Vaughan. In fact, they think it is so big that they want to involve the police.'

'No. I will not have the police involved with one of my friends. I won't hear of it. In fact I won't allow it.'

'Phoebe, you can't stop them. They are the auditors and they will have the final say with their recommendations. It is a public company and they have a duty to report anything illegal.'

'I will never speak to you again,' she snapped.

I must admit, deep down I thought that was a wonderful idea. I only wish now I had told her so.

The cheque books were never found and even when I interviewed Williams about the auditor's findings and feelings on the matter, he brazened it out saying he knew nothing of it,

Further investigations revealed that the auditors had so far discovered that Vaughan Williams had embezzled over eighteen thousand pounds from the firm. I didn't tell Phoebe until I had suspended him on full pay and even then he sneered and said, 'It's a flea bite to you DAVID STEPHENS.'

What made things worse, he had the brassed-face gall to still come to our house to play bridge with Phoebe. I couldn't believe it and said directly to him in front of the others, 'Mr. Williams you are not welcome here until matters are sorted out at Pennington's. With the police now involved, I don't want you near any of my family until the embezzlement question has been sorted out.'

'You think you are god almighty, don't you?' he said in his annoying, almost artificial, Welsh accent. 'Just because you've got a big house and money you think you can dictate to everyone. Well, you can't dictate to me. If the police are involved you will regret it, because it will all come out. I'll expose everything you are doing and then we'll see how high and mighty you are then.'

'Whatever you say, that's up to you, but you are a thief, so get out of my house.'

Phoebe's other friends looked on in stark amazement; they had never seen me so angry and determined before. Even Phoebe was very quiet and did not make any comment before or after. I made one last foray into the fray, when I told them we believed that he had taken in excess if eighteen thousand pounds. They were agog, commenting to Phoebe, 'Why on earth did David put up with him for so long?'

Even after all that had been said, she was still reluctant to believe that it was true, in fact she put up such a defence of his character that I was convinced that her relationship was more than platonic. I didn't care if it was true as I had fallen in love with Constance. But I could never prove any relationship between them and I suppose as I was not that bothered I didn't even try.

I appointed a new accountant, in fact I promoted the young lady who was Williams's deputy, and she did a wonderful job and it gave encouragement to the other workers as they could see we rewarded good work.

Chapter 6

The court case against Vaughan Williams was a messy affair, but the outcome was in no doubt and he had come over as a very jealous and devious man. Even the judge made the comment that he had bitten the hand that fed him, but it was when he was giving evidence on his own behalf and said, 'They wouldn't miss it and everyone can see they've got enough,' that the judge in his sentencing commented that he was a man who carried an enormous chip on his shoulder.

The insurance company paid out for the loss of money, which turned out to be thirty-one thousand pounds, and from my point of view that was the end of the matter, but they sued him through the courts and sold his house to pay them back.

I did at one time feel sorry for him as he lost his wife and family, couldn't get another job and spent much of his time getting drunk, ending up a bitter, vengeful man. He always pontificating how pompous I was and how much money we had, and he even turned his attention against Phoebe, telling the world what a spoilt woman she was – to anyone who would listen that was.

I am sure he would have been happy to see me in my present state, but I heard he hadn't lived that long after his downfall.

It was as a result of the Vaughan Williams affair that I took my father's advice and appointed a new managing director of Pennington's, to replace me. I realised that I could no longer be one hundred per cent efficient in running the business; I couldn't keep my finger on the button of all departments so it was really in everybody's interest that I stood down.

I gave him an extraordinary bonus to ensure his loyalty to the firm, which in turn would give me more time to do other things, and it worked. Peter Wilcox became my right-arm man and at the tender age of thirty seven he had bags of energy and enthusiasm. I moved myself upstairs as it were, and became president.

I had learned a lot from my father, when I took over from him all those years ago, and one lesson in particular. You cannot give a person the responsibility without giving him the authority to do the job. In other words, Wilcox got a free hand and would sink or swim by his own efforts. Fortunately, he swam.

Constance and I had put the shares I had given her in a nominated account under the name of Terence Pendlebury, our solicitor, to avoid any difficulties on the voting aspects. Why she still insisted I had the income from any shares I will never know, but I gave it to Phoebe, to purge my guilt I suppose, although I never really felt guilty. In fact, I just thought it would be one of the ways I could get her out of my system. The more I gave her the more she would stay away.

Life carried on much as it ever did, except that on a couple of occasions I got up in the middle of the night and drove to Pennington's and went to my office. I don't know why I was there and when I came out of my trance – as I will call it – I felt totally confused. On the second occasion the security section had called the police believing me to be an intruder. They arrived and found me in the office asleep. Naturally they were worried and escorted me home, much to the embarrassment of Phoebe. The housekeeper answered the door but they insisted that Phoebe came and spoke to them.

'We've brought your husband home, madam. We think he is ill and may need a doctor,' one of them said when Phoebe eventually deigned to come to the door.

'No he's not,' she snapped and pulled me, in slamming the door in their faces.

'Don't you embarrass me like that again, what are the neighbours going to think if they see a police car here? Are you that stupid?'

I began to have severe personality changes, not all the time but now and again. I think they may have been brought on by stress. Anyway, the first one began there and then. I had never been violent in word or deed, but I remember shouting back at Phoebe, using words I had never ever used before: 'Oh shut your fucking mouth, you bloody whore! I don't care what the fucking neighbours think. Now fuck off.' I remember I couldn't believe I'd said it; it wasn't like me, but afterwards, I was damn glad I had as she went to her room absolutely shocked.

I went back to bed and slept until midday and was only woken when I heard Phoebe telling everyone to be quiet and not to wake me up. My mind knew what I had done and even though it was Phoebe that had to face the barrage of my abuse, I was really sorry; but my brain wouldn't let me remember, so I got up as though nothing had happened.

I went into the breakfast room and picked up the morning paper to be greeted by Mrs Cripp.

'Hello, David. Do you feel better?'

'I haven't been ill.'

She looked surprised and even more so when I asked for a full English breakfast.

God knows why I said 'a full English'. I must have thought that I was in France with my Constance, but it caused great concern,

'Do you mean bacon and egg?'

'Of course I do,' I replied, somewhat annoyed.

'You're not doing anything of the sort, Mrs Cripp. He is too late for breakfast; it's nearly lunchtime. And furthermore I am not going to be spoken to like that again. Not in my house,' Phoebe said, following me into the breakfast room.

'Bacon and eggs please, Phyllis,' I repeated.

'No, Mrs Cripp,'Phoebe shouted. 'He is not to have it in here.'

I turned round and manhandled her out of the room, pushing her hard, and causing her to fall over as she went through the open door.

'Bacon and egg please, Phyllis, and I'm sorry you were put in this position.'

I sat down and fifteen minutes later breakfast arrived, which by now I had lost all interest in, but when the bitch came back in and shouted, 'Can't you hurry up? I've got people coming for lunch.' Well that was the excuse for several cups of tea and a much longer meal than normal.

It was only when she shouted 'Hurry up' that I lost it again.

'Use the fucking kitchen,' I shouted, and with that I threw all the plates on the floor and one at her, the bitch.

I went into the lounge and sat down, unable to remember anything of what I had said or done, but I still had to listen to the Phoebe's onslaught, which was especially awful as I was now back to normal.

I heard Phoebe ordering Mrs Cripp to clean the mess up quickly as the guests were arriving soon, with Mrs Cripp trying to say that she thought I was ill and should see a doctor

Phoebe replied, 'Nonsense. There's nothing wrong with him and anyway it is none of your affair.' She then turned to me and snapped, 'And I don't want you spoiling my luncheon with my friends.'

'Don't worry. I'll keep out of the way.'

I remember locking myself in my study and lapsing into thought, knowing that my only solace was when w – that is, Constance and I – were together. I no longer had any relationship with my sons; they were now well and truly married with families of their own and I rarely saw them. But I did have a much closer one with my daughter.

Hannah knew what I was going through and knew there was something wrong with me. She also knew that I was involved with someone else. In fact she knew I was going out with Constance. I remember it so well, the day she came and sat on the arm of my chair, put her arm around my shoulders and asked, 'What's the matter, Dad?'

'It doesn't matter, love, you don't want to listen to my troubles.'

'Come on, please dad, tell me,' she asked again. This was followed by a few minutes of verbal fencing and then I actually confessed my problems for the first time to anyone other than my father, mother and Constance.

'I don't know how long I have before it really gets worse, but I've already started having personality changes so I'm told. I am trying hard and Constance spends at least a couple of hours a day helping me with the memory tests, but I am beginning to find even these things more difficult.'

I don't know whether I did the right thing or not in telling Hannah of my worries, and I don't know whether it was this that spurred to hurry into marriage, but she did make the comment that she wanted me to walk down the aisle with her on my arm.

I was worried about her and the man she had chosen, Donald Frobisher. He was twenty five and had never done a day's work in his life; he had simply lived off benefits. He came from a respectable sort of background and when we met his parents for the first time they seemed reasonable enough.

Hannah was now ready and keen to join the firm and I had the job of asking Peter, the managing director, if he would permit it, or should I say offer her a job.

I explained the situation to Hannah after she had said, 'But Dad, you're the boss.'

'No, I am not love, not any more. Peter is and he will be the one who decides. If he says no, well I am sorry. I cannot do the job properly anymore.'

Anyway, I remember Peter told me she was worth a try and he put her on six months' probation, which she passed with flying colours and never looked back. She was like me in that respect and became an asset to the firm in all ways.

I confided everything in Constance telling her about Hannah

and Pennington's and how thrilled I was that she had taken such an interest in the firm and had done so well. To my sheer delight, Constance made her will in favour of Hannah, giving her back the family shares and actually intimated that she would give them to her when she thought she was responsible enough to have them, with the proviso that her young man couldn't get his hands on them should they part.

Everything seemed to be done in too much of a hurry, especially with the wedding. When she told me she always wanted me to walk her down the aisle and did not want to risk the possibility of that not happening, it made me feel terrible and I wished I hadn't said anything to her.

The day was fast arriving and plans were being dutifully made and we even had to have an expert to assist Phoebe with all the arrangements. Even so, Hannah wanted a quiet wedding and thankfully overruled her mother as much as possible, much to Phoebe's annoyance, especially when the guest list was being drawn up. One surprise guest on Hannah's list was Constance and for the first time Phoebe showed some concern as to why.

In spite of all Hannah's efforts to keep the numbers low, Phoebe managed to have over a hundred invited guests.

I was to be the proud father who was giving my daughter away to an absolute shit. I wish I had said something and tried to persuade her not to get involved, but I always had the philosophy of letting the children make their own minds up. It was a big mistake as all he seems to have wanted was to get his greasy hands on my money, but he was to be another one in for a big surprise.

Now where was I? Come on, come on think man. Oh yes, I had to take her, the evil one, to help decorate the church and we were late.

*

It was that constant dictatorial voice that she always put on that got to me. I know I should have done something about it at the very beginning but it was easier to just walk away, for peace and quiet.

'Come on, David, hurry up'

I remember walking out to the car, getting into it and suddenly asking, 'Have I locked the house?'

'Of course you have; now come on.'

'Sorry. I'll have to go and check.'

The door was locked and that was another occasion when I showed real signs of what was to come; especially when I had to go back for a second time to check again and had to suffer that woman shouting at me. I felt so confused and because of it I found myself driving to my office at Pennington's and received another tirade of mental abuse before at last arriving at the church some thirty minutes late.

I heard Phoebe apologising to everybody in her superior way and saying it was my fault, I was useless, and she had to do everything as usual.

I remember the wedding went well except I made a mess of my speech, or should I say I repeated a part of it on two and a half occasions, before Hannah helped me out; but fortunately I managed to get the sympathy vote by declaring that things had got a little too much for me. Then I heard Phoebe complaining once again to one of her friends and then to our son, that I was a bloody nuisance and could no longer be trusted to do anything.

I can't forget a day or two after the wedding when I went to see my parents. There was no special reason for the visit, but I will never forget that it turned out to be one of the worst moments of my life. We were sitting in their lounge taking tea when my dad said, 'David your mother is worried about you; she thinks you are unwell. Are you all right?'

I sat quietly for a few moments wondering what to do, I still didn't really want to burden them with my troubles and they were becoming very old, and whilst at that moment everything working well with no sign of my complaint. I thought I could still avoid telling them; but before I knew it I broke down and blurted out that I had dementia. They came and sat on the arms of my chair, put their arms round my shoulders and stayed there for several minutes whilst I cried and cried. I remember resting my head on my mother as she stroked my brow with my father squeezing my hand to give me courage.

It was only when my mother said naively that the children would look after me that I came to my senses.

'Mother dear, my children, apart from Hannah, would not give me the time of day. All they want is what I can give them financially. They are just like their mother. Anyway they have their own lives to lead and I wouldn't want them to do anything. I have made provisions for when I become senile; I will have twenty-four hour nursing until I die.'

We sat in silence for what seemed like minutes as they took in what was happening to me, before my mother, a typical wartime lady, said, 'David, would you like another cup of tea? It always helps you know.'

'Of course I will, Mother.'

She left the room and we could both hear her crying and fumbling around in the kitchen, the shock of what she had heard taking hold.

My dad stayed with me until she returned, trying to comfort me, which made things worse, as I felt so upset for them. It was when he said, 'David, as long as I am here I will always help you. You know that don't you?'

'Of course I do, Dad. But you mustn't worry. I will be all right and there are lots of new drugs which will help me to stop things getting out of hand.'

I knew by the squeeze of his hand that he didn't believe there was anything that could help me in the long run and he knew I was just trying to stop him from worrying.

My mother returned her eyes red from her tears she'd tried

to hide. I got up and hugged her; she couldn't hide them this time.

'Mum, don't worry, please, I'll be all right, Constance will look after me, I know she will; so don't worry.'

'More than that other bloody woman, you mark my words,' my father said angrily.

We chatted about this and that for well over an hour, none of us wanting to talk about my dementia and yet it was the most important thing on our minds.

As I left, they both hugged me as if it was for the last time and I could see in my mirror they didn't dare go in until my car had disappeared from view, despite the rain.

I wished to god that I hadn't told them as I'm sure it was the worry of it all that killed my father. He died a few months after and my mother just six months after him. It was as though life had been taken from her and she just lost the will to live. I remember a little poem when I was at school, which seemed very apt for this occasion.

> He first deceased,
> she for a little tried,
> to live without him,
> liked it not and died.

I was told that the average man is lucky if he can count on more than one hand the number of true friends in his or her life, so I know I was lucky. I had James Percival, I had Mr Pennington, I've got Hannah, I had my Mum and Dad and I've lost them and it was my fault, but I have got my Constance.

'David, what's the matter, why are you crying?' a nurse asked as she entered my room.

'I was thinking about my mother and father.'

'David you have spoken to me, that's wonderful,' she remarked, having seldom heard me speak, if ever.

'I was just remembering what wonderful friends they were and how much I loved them. They wouldn't have left me in here.'

'Tell me about them,' she said, trying to prolong the conversation.

But I couldn't carry on; it all stopped there.

I knew what I wanted to say but it wouldn't come out. Really all I wanted was to tell her that I loved them dearly and wished they were here.

She gave up very quickly, not like my Constance, she wouldn't have done so.

Where is Constance? I've just remembered I haven't seen her for days.

'CONSTANCE!' I shouted.

'David, you mustn't shout like that. You will disturb the other patients. Come on now, lie down. It's time to go to sleep. I'm going to put your light out now. Is that all right?'

Damn! I can't answer; my brain has slipped out of gear. Sorry nurse. Nurse Bell, she's one of the better ones; the trouble is everyone wants her, so we all get too little. She tries, she always tells us what she is going to do and why; always involves us and speaks to us like Constance does. Oh where is my Constance?

Chapter 7

'Good morning, David, do you feel any better today?' Nurse Bell asked.

She had come to start the bloody daily ritual of getting me up, taking me to the toilet in case I forgot and did it in the bed; then plonking me down in the bloody chair, so that I could stare out of the window for the rest of the day. Oh, what an existence!

'David, you were very upset last night; you were crying much of the night. Can you remember what upset you?'

Ah, that explains why my pillow was wet through, and my handkerchief. Now, what upset me?

'Come on, David, think about it, see if you can remember. Were you thinking about your mother and father again?'

I'm trying to for god's sake. Yes, I do remember. I was thinking about my parents.

'Yes, I was.'

'Tell me about them.'

'They were always there for me, right until the end.'

'Don't cry again, David. Give me your hand. Now look at me, I am going to come back later on and we will have a good chat. All right?'

'Yes.'

'I promise. See you later; I must finish my work first. 'Bye'

Why was I thinking about my mother and father? Oh, I remember, I was trying to keep myself sane, thinking about my life.

Now where was I? Ah yes, I had told them I had dementia. That's it.

Dementia they call it. I wouldn't wish it on my worst enemy. To be dependent for everything just to keep you alive, when there is no cure, is awful and it's not particular whom it attacks; Granville Peterson the former prime minister is in here. He's much worse than me. No one talks about him and some of the staff don't even know who he is. What a life he must have had and what stories he could tell. I wonder if my story would be so interesting.

Anyway, back when I told my parents about my illness, I was still reasonably OK. I had regular appointments with James Percival and for the first time he told me to go away again and to take Constance with me. At least he could see how it had benefited me the last time I went with her. Well, to me it was doctor's orders and I just did that. Phoebe was absolutely delighted that I would be out of her hair and couldn't wait to get rid of me.

Constance really did work hard and I know in my heart she was doing everything possible to help me, but I knew the irreversible process was getting worse. I could be fine for weeks then I seemed to have a bad patch, which would last progressively longer each time; at this moment anything from five to twenty minutes, but during that time I know it was dreadful for all those around me. I knew I shouldn't be doing certain things, but while my mind was telling me that, my brain was making me do them anyway.

It seemed I was becoming two different people in one body, a Dr Jekyll and Mr Hyde syndrome. I could control the one but not the other.

After the two-hour flight to Nice, followed by the hour taxi drive to La Croix Valmer, we were once again like two young lovers – until I couldn't remember where I was. I was lost in my own house. Constance went into panic. She began giving me every test she could. Every few minutes it was question and answer and I know she brought me round, but it was frightening; what was so warming was when she told me, 'I'll never let you down, whatever happens.' It was moments like that that I could cling to. It helped to restore my waning confidence.

People don't appreciate how quickly you lose your confidence. I know they remember seeing me as the managing director of Pennington's with all the importance that held, if that really did matter in the broad spectre of things. I realise that nothing is important in anyone's life except love, friendship and health. Anyway, they would have seen me making speeches in front of hundreds, making business decisions that affected hundreds, and they could not imagine that I was now almost scared of my own shadow, almost scared of making any decision. I found I could only do that when I had Constance with me. She had so quickly become my security blanket. The worse I got, the more I clung on to the security blanket, and then on days I thought it may not be there, that's when I would feel at my worst.

Now what was I thinking before I interrupted myself? Ah yes, I was once again in France and we had arrived at La Croix. I remember I seemed to recover after that first confusion and with my Constance's help and patience we had another lovely time.

I decided we should visit St Paul de Vence, just outside Nice. It is a wonderful little ex-fortified village built on top of a hill, overlooking some beautiful countryside and I'm sure it is the centre of the art world on Cote d'Azur, as almost every building, housed one artist after another, from the modern and the new impressionist to the portrait. It was this latter type that I was interested in.

On our first visit to Cavalaire, we had had our photo taken sitting in a little restaurant by the harbour. It was a beautiful photo with me leaning over the table with my head resting on my hand and I was just looking at Constance like someone in love, which I was. We commissioned an artist to paint a picture from it for us, giving him full discretion; at the same time I was just so proud that I told him I was in love with her and to my utter surprise he told us he could see that. That made it for me, I was in seventh heaven and I loved being in love. The picture would take about three months to complete and he, John Patrick Gauthier, the artist, would phone Constance once it was finished.

To celebrate this commission, I was told to get ready as she was going to treat me to dinner that evening and we were to be ready for six thirty. I remember that I discovered later that Hannah had organised the whole shindig as she was in the area at the time. The taxi duly arrived on time and we were whisked away once more to Nice. I can't quite remember but I think it was to the Negresco hotel on the Promenade des Anglais over-looking the sea. We were met by the doorman who opened the taxi doors and escorted us in. We sat in the lounge with a wonderful bottle of champagne and were then joined by Hannah and her boss, Peter Wilcox, who were celebrating that she had just won a wonderful order. I hugged her, the tears running down my face, she knew my plight and was another on my side.

When I look back, I was in my sixties and despite all my wealth, I had never experienced such a wonderful time before. We had a lovely meal followed by a memorable dance, two further bottles of champagne, and still I had a further surprise. Constance had booked us all a room for the night. It was the first time I felt naughty and I made the most of it. It was another of those lovely warm evenings where you could take your jacket off and stroll along the long flat palm-tree lined promenade, only on this occasion we took off our shoes and walked to the sea. With Constance on my arm I didn't notice the pebbles and as our feet touched the water, I turned and kissed her,

'Thank you, darling, for a wonderful evening,' I said kissing her again and gently pulling her into the sea.

She screamed with delight as we both fell into the water and once again kissed. The shoreline was lit by the hundreds of lamps on the promenade and from the restaurants on the beach. I could tell we were almost spotlighted in the sea, but that didn't matter, we were in love and it was wonderful. I can't imagine what people thought as we took most of our clothes off and walked across the road back to the Negresco, simply wearing our underclothes; I did however have my jacket, as any gentleman would, and I gave it to my lover. But explaining that we had fallen into the sea was difficult, especially as half the population of Nice must have seen us running in. Of course, no one believed us, but it was decadent and it was exciting. We sunk into the enormous bath and then once again I could not resist the softness of her skin, the scent of her perfume and her wonderful delicate, sensuous touch.

I remember that night more than any as it was ruined by my waking up at three in the morning and screaming at the top of my voice, 'CONSTANCE.' Suddenly, I was terrified and didn't know where I was and thought I was alone. But Constance was next to me and immediately threw her arms around me and comforted me, like one would a young child. I came too very quickly once I could see her.

'You had a bad dream, that's all it was,' she said, as we were disturbed by a knock on the door from one of the porters.

'*Vous allez bien?*' (Is everything OK?), he asked.

'*Mon mari est malade. C'est un cauchemar,*' Constance answered in her best French.

Those words, I remember, meant everything to me. It was the first time she had referred to me as her husband and it made me feel so secure. However, there were more enquiries about my welfare, but by now I was back on this earth and I was able to answer them myself, apologising for my nuisance, but not knowing what I had done. I knew I had done something stupid but what had it been? It had even brought Hannah to the room.

'Dad, are you OK?'

'Of course he is. He's just had a terrible nightmare, haven't you, darling?' Constance replied, bringing me into the conversation and then insisting I tell Hannah what happened. I couldn't as yet remember but even at three in the morning Constance made me think about it until I got it right.

She realised from the word go that it was very important to include me in the conversations and make me answer the questions that were put to me. She would never allow anybody to answer for me regardless of whom it was, but would always help me if I was in difficulty. Our friends, our real friends that is, began to understand what Constance was doing and could see the benefit it gave me and some of them even did the same. None of the bitch's lot ever tried to help me, though; they were all tarred with the same brush.

Hannah left after a few minutes and I heard her say, 'You are an angel and I can see why he loves you.'

Again, it's things like that which have stuck in my memory.

I was glad when we returned to La Croix with its security of being a familiar place, but here again I had another warning of things to come. Constance had popped into the village and left me in the garden pottering, weeding, that sort of thing, and when she returned a few minutes later I was sitting in a chair just staring into space, looking totally vacant.

'Come on, David, get up, move yourself, you can do it.' She put her arms underneath my armpits and pulled me out of the chair and slowly got me walking while she supported me.

'Well done, sweetheart, I knew you could do it.'

It was as though my brain did not want to tell the other parts of my body what to do. I knew what was wanted, I could see it, I could imagine it, I could think it, but I couldn't communicate it, and I couldn't say anything. I could now see the worry in Constance's eyes as she struggled with me, but once again the spell was broken as Simone came on the scene and I clicked into real time.

One night I was lying in bed with Constance when suddenly I got out of bed.

'Where are my shoes?'

'What do you want your shoes for?' she asked.

'I just want to be sure.'

'Sure of what, darling?'

'In case I need them,'

'Oh I see. They are in the hall where you left them.'

I remember trundling off into the hall and coming back proud as punch. 'I've got them.'

'Good, come back to bed, darling.'

I remember getting back into bed and was just about to lie down when I asked, 'Have I got a clean shirt?'

'Yes, darling, it's in your drawer.'

'Where's my drawer?'

'Just over there, darling, by the big wardrobe,' she replied, trying to almost spell things out to make it easier for me.

I then took out the shirt, cuddled it for a second or two and then put it with my shoes. 'You never know when we will have to get up quickly, do you?'

'No, darling, you don't. Come back to bed now and cuddle up. I'm glad you sorted that out.'

That little bit of praise made me feel good and I popped back into bed and went to sleep.

Constance's first job was to make an appointment for us to visit Miss Lovejoy, the woman recommended by Andrew to help with the memory training, and as it was only three days away we packed everything up and returned home with Lovejoy's assistance, being foremost in Constance's mind.

I hated being left by her. Yes, that's it, the defining moment, that's when I changed. That subtle difference came to the fore. Previously I would say or think, I hate leaving her, now it was, I hate being left by her. I sensed that my confidence was beginning to ebb away.

I arrived back at home to the usual sort of welcome, except this time it was, 'I didn't expect you this week. Has Hannah come back with you?'

Thank god I was all there at this moment.

'She left me at the airport in Nice,' I replied, fingers crossed. 'No doubt she will ring you when she gets back.'

'I'm having a dinner party tonight and I didn't expect you,' she added, waiting for me to take a lead.

'Don't worry, I'll make my own arrangements.'

This was another wonderful opportunity to see my lover, which I took gladly. And I spent the rest of the day to the late evening in her company, just watching television until it was time to go home.

The latter I did not want to do and almost had another stressful relapse. Constance took me home at about ten o'clock and Mrs Cripp answered the door.

'I've found David, he's a bit lost,' she said, squeezing my hand and whispering, 'Don't worry, I love you,' whilst Mrs Cripp went to fetch Phoebe from her guests.

'Don't leave him here; take him into the kitchen, out of the way.'

Constance shuddered at the comment and I even saw Mrs Cripp wince at Phoebe's behaviour. Constance reluctantly left me in the tender care of our housekeeper and I remember I simply went to my room.

Unbeknown to me, Constance had made an appointment to see both Andrew and James to discuss the recent events, the former increasing the dosage of the pills I had been taking, which he thought would stabilise my condition a little, and possibly cut down the number of incidents. He also thought my 'best friend', as he always jokingly called Constance, was doing a good job.

James was wonderful. I could see he hated seeing me in this condition and he devised a plan to help and I remember thinking if the General Medical Council had heard about it, he would have been struck off.

He was also shocked that I hadn't told Phoebe and insisted that if his scheme was to work she must be told and so for the first time I went to the doctor's along with my wife.

James was astonished at her callousness and sheer coldness toward me. She talked constantly as though I was already an imbecile and not in the room.

'How long has he got before he is a cabbage? He'll have to be put in a home.'

James and I winked at each other, as he knew the contents of my will.

'Phoebe, David has made arrangements for him to be nursed and looked after at home, and when necessary for twenty-four hours a day.'

'I am not having him nursed in my house,' she said, somewhat haughtily.

'Phoebe,' I said, 'it is my home too, as you well know.'

'No. I won't hear of it.'

'Look you are going to need some help and now it is very important you do so, because the more David keeps his brain active, the more he will be able to do, and the less likely it will be that he needs nursing.'

This is where I know he would have had his fingers crossed.

'It is *really* important that he has constant companionship, someone to talk to him, to get him to do things and keep him active. There is one of your friends, Phoebe, who will fit the bill well. A woman called Constance Redpath. She has had a lot of experience in these matters. I know how busy you are and that it would be impossible for you to devote the time to David he needs now, so it would make sense to let Constance help.'

He looked at me and smiled, but I could see through that smile, not only was he doing it to help me, but also he wanted to ensure I had the most possible happiness in what was the rest of my short life.

'Well, I'll have to do something, I suppose. I'm not going to be able to put up with this for long, especially if it gets worse,' Phoebe snapped.

James then explained the symptoms of what might happen, to which she confessed I had already been aggressive toward her.

She was told I may not know her, and also in no uncertain terms to expect the unexpected.

'David is aware it will get worse. Shall I give Constance a ring for you?'

'Oh no. I'll see to it the moment we get back,' Phoebe replied.

After a few more do's and don'ts we left the surgery with Phoebe terrified out of her wits.

'I'll call round to see Constance now, she won't mind.'

'Shouldn't you ring her first and warn her?'

She took no notice and went immediately to Constance's house. I was beginning to feel I was about to have another episode, brought on by the stress, by the worry of Constance not being warned of what the doctor had said and not being prepared for the might of Phoebe.

We arrived at her house and thankfully she was in. I was stuck; once again I was staring into space, totally vacant and unable to move. I saw Constance at the door, but I was unable to do anything except look. I remember I heard Phoebe call me but I couldn't move. She came running back to the car in panic, unable to think straight.

'Constance,' she yelled, 'can you help me, please? David can't move.'

Constance came quickly to the car, taking control of the situation. She opened the car door, spun me around, lifting my legs out of the car, and put her arms around me and gently pulled me upright.

'Come on, darling, try and walk towards me,' she said holding me firmly as she steadied me along.

Phoebe hadn't noticed the sincerity in the word 'darling'; she was too busy being concerned about her future and perhaps still in panic. This attack lasted about five minutes before I came back to normal and all the time Phoebe was muttering to herself, 'What am I going to do?' 'He'll have to go in a home.' 'Constance can you help me?'

We were invited in and sat in her lounge with the French

windows open. Constance lived in a peaceful part of the town, just on the edge of the country. In fact, her house was in the green belt and I could hear the birds singing and was once again confident now that I knew I could see Constance regularly.

'Of course I'll help,' she told Phoebe. 'What do you want me to do?'

Phoebe then gave her a whole list of instructions as if Constance was an employee and not a friend offering help, but she took it on the chin and just to be cheeky, I suggested that Phoebe could pay her expenses. I don't know where I got the courage to get involved or to suggest that my best friend should get paid.

'Can you start straight away? I've got a dinner party tonight and David will only be in the way?'

Constance was appalled at what she had said and I was too. Whilst I was never really happy with Phoebe, I would never knowingly hurt her and I found it very hurtful the way she spoke about me, and it was always as if I was not there and it didn't matter to her in any event.

'Shall I have him to stay at my house tonight, Phoebe, would that help? '

'Oh, that's a good idea, do you mind?'

'Of course not, I'll bring him back tomorrow'

'Constance, you are a darling. What on earth would I do without you?' And with that she was gone, without a word to me.

I couldn't believe my luck, my doctor, albeit my friend had got my dragon wife to sanction a wonderful night with my lover.

There wasn't the mad rush in the forest or the fun in the sea, we were just there behaving as man and wife alone together, sitting in the garden, taking tea, without an apparent care in the world, for the moment at least. It was sheer heaven.

I remember sitting on the settee in front of the television with Constance nuzzled close to me, something I had never ever done with Phoebe; in fact I don't ever remember sitting on a settee with her alone at any time. For me this was a special moment.

'You don't mind if I don't make the bed up in the next room do you, David? I thought it would be better if you slept in my bed with me. It would at least enable us to get to know each other better and I could keep you warm in a strange bed.'

'Well, I don't know, what would the neighbours think?'

'I haven't got any neighbours.' She continued nuzzling a bit closer. 'Well I never, David, you haven't brought any pyjamas or your toothbrush.'

I grabbed her like some naughty excited child.

'I'll just ring Phoebe, it'll look better if we ask for them.' I was determined not to let go of her, the excitement of the moment was too much.

'Come on, let me phone her.'

Constance phoned Phoebe and within minutes Chris the handyman was at the front door. It was as though she couldn't get rid of me quick enough; out of the house and out of her life.

Constance brought me down to earth with a bump. 'Where are your tablets?'

'I don't know.'

'When did you last take one?'

'I don't know.'

'David, darling, have you taken any?'

'I don't know.'

'Come on, I'm taking you home, I want to get these pills.'

'I don't want to go. Please, Constance, I don't want to go.' What was I saying for god's sake? I knew we were only going for pills and that she wouldn't leave me, I just couldn't stop myself.

'Don't be silly, darling, come on, the sooner we are there, the sooner we will be back.'

We got into the car and drove quickly to my home. I couldn't believe it, what a welcome we received.

'Oh my god, can't you cope already?' Phoebe snapped as though I was not there.

'Mother, don't talk about Father like that.'

My god, who's he? He must be one of the guests. I wonder

what it is in aid of? Good god it's Josh my son. I didn't recognise him.

'Of course I can,' Constance replied, 'but I understand David has to take some very important pills and he hasn't got them. Can we have them, please?'

'Of course you can, but hurry; I have a lot to do.'

Then suddenly I could speak. 'Hello, Josh, it's been a long time, I thought you were one of the—'

'Sorry Dad. I've been so busy,' he interrupted me and thank god he didn't realise I hadn't recognised him at first. He thought I was being a little sarcastic at not seeing him.

'Come on, come on.' The Dragon said as she escorted us up to my bedroom and started looking for the tablets. 'What are they called?'

'Smart Pills, I believe,' Constance replied.

We searched for several minutes with Phoebe becoming more and more agitated, as they were nowhere to be found.

'Can't we hurry, my guests will be arriving soon and I don't want him around when they do.'

I could see Constance flinching at the crass cruelty of what Phoebe was doing and saying, then to my horror, I found the pills in my pocket. I realised that I had caused everyone some difficulty and proceeded to announce 'Here they are,' as though I had just found them, but Constance had seen me. She didn't say anything at the time, but later, after Phoebe had commented, 'Thank god, I must get on,' and we returned to Constance's home, she tore into me.

'You little tinker,' she snapped at me like some school ma'am addressing a naughty pupil. 'I will have to smack your bottom,' she said as we went through the front door and immediately ran into the lounge falling on to the settee. We were once again like two teenagers until I found things difficult and felt embarrassed.

'Come on, David, hug me, it doesn't matter, just hug me and give me one of those lovely kisses that I fell in love with.'

I remember those lovely words, they were full of meaning and with her caresses and kisses all over my naked body things in the end became special.

We lay locked in each other's arms, French windows open allowing the last of the summer's warm day to gently cool our passion and to allow us to stay close, for what seemed like hours. I couldn't have wished for anything better in my life, except that I would have wanted it to last forever.

Being with her was like being married, but Constance soon had to become businesslike, prepare the evening meal, make sure I took my medication and keep on with the incessant memory tests and conversation, but I loved it; if only it hadn't been a means to an end.

Late the following morning we had not heard from any of my family so Constance phoned Phoebe.

'Phoebe, darling, David has to go to see a specialist today for his weekly memory training sessions, shall we come round or would you like me to go with him?

'Oh you go. Is it any trouble?'

'Not at all; he's no trouble. By the way he slept like a baby last night,' she added, squeezing my hand and giving me a knowing grin.

Later that day we arrived at Miss Dorothy Lovejoy's to start the first of the many sessions I would have with her. She was a jovial person but thorough and professional; everything she did or said from the word go was for a reason and measured. I soon realised this was to see how fast the disease was progressing. She lived and operated from her semi-detached house in a quiet suburb in the neighbouring town of Warstones. It was a comfortable house and I'm sure designed to make people feel at ease. Everything was relaxed and there was no rush; she had allocated as much time as I felt I could cope with.

Her secretary had introduced us as Mr and Mrs Stephens and we had let it stand as we enjoyed the thought that we were a proper couple.

The tests began much as they had at the specialist's, simple ones to begin with, growing more difficult as the questions progressed. Every time I got one right you would have thought I had passed my School Certificate; she was so pleased for me. She didn't let me know my failures, which I was aware of, but couldn't respond to. Instead she directed my training effort in that direction, which really was to be Constance's work with me.

She then asked Constance all my personal details, which normally only a real wife would know, and she was delighted that I was still sexually active, with the added caveat that occasionally it was difficult.

'It is important we maintain our normal relationships as long as possible,' she commented, to which I remember adding that I was all for it, which caused my 'new wife' to scold me: 'That's enough of that.'

'Now, Mrs Stephens, may I call you Constance?'

'Yes, of course.'

'I know David is fully aware of his situation and he knows what efforts he has to make to stave off the disease, but I really want to talk to you about your problems and how you will suffer too. Because whichever way we look at this, it is a joint effort and it is the only way either of you will cope well.'

I remember feeling dreadful that I was putting Constance through this but the reassuring squeeze of her hand while we were listening to Miss Lovejoy really did give me strength. I knew I had to do as I was told because to fail and end up like a vegetable was to awful to contemplate.

'David has already realised his confidence is taking a knock, haven't you, David?'

I nodded agreement.

'And I'm sure you must feel vulnerable.'

I nodded again.

'Well, Constance,' went on Miss Lovejoy, 'it is very important he is reassured. David will need to retain his identity and his dignity at all times. It is obvious to me, David, that you are used to wearing a jacket and tie and if that is case, then you must continue to do so. I know it will be troublesome, but it is worth the effort. Do you feel better after a wash and shave, and when you have put your tie on?'

'Yes, funnily enough I do.'

'Then it is essential that you keep that bit of personal pride in your appearance.

'Constance, you must never talk down to David or talk about him when he can hear you. That is fatal. Try to avoid scolding and criticising him and if you have to, never say it in front of others, whoever they may be. If you do, it will destroy him. You must ensure David retains his dignity at all times. If he's on the toilet, knock and say can I come in. Get his authority to do things; it will make him feel important. It is good for David's self-esteem. David is strong now, but maybe later it will be a different matter. What do you think so far, David?'

'It's no good pretending, I am worried, but I know I can bear it if I have Constance to help me.'

'You have to do a lot for yourself, David, and it won't be easy. One or two other things, Constance, which I am sure you are doing already, such as the brain exercises, Sudoku, crosswords, general knowledge; they are all very good, so you must stick to them. I mention them for completeness. Do things together as much as you can. Always involve David in the decision-making process, no matter how trivial it may seem. Keep a life history book and if you have the time, write things down that you did that day and talk about them and also things that David will remember from his past so that you can talk about them too.

'You will note one important thing that I have done. Can you think what that is, David?'

I was on top form at this moment and replied, 'I can't think of anything specific, but you have said "David" a lot.'

'That's it. Well done, David. Well done. This is a very important point for everyone who cares for sufferers of this disease. Don't keep referring to David as he, him or his; always use David's name; then he won't forget it.'

It was all very worrying; everything Miss Lovejoy told us was the opposite of what Phoebe did to me. Everything! I hadn't got a chance at home. I really had to be with Constance as she was already doing all Miss Lovejoy was telling us was important, it was my only chance.

Constance was lovely during this little talk; on every little point Miss Lovejoy made, she would turn to me and squeeze my hand and give me a beautiful smile.

Oh god. I can feel myself starting to cry. If they see me doing that we'll have another inquest. It will be, 'Are you all right, David?' in that condescending way that some of the nurses speak to all of us older or infirm patients. And always in a loud voice so that the rest of the bloody hospital knows you are having problems.

Why the bloody hell am I here? That's better, now where was I? That's it, Lovejoy's place.

Miss Lovejoy had told us that we should try and help each other and then gave us a long list of things we had to do and practise on the TYM procedure, and from then on we were to see her once a fortnight.

Everything was as near normal as possible as we left Miss Lovejoy's but I realised I was going to put whoever was looking after me through a great deal of misery, and I was beginning to think I couldn't do this to Constance. In fact, I was very glad I had made arrangements to be looked after by a specialist nurse.

'I can't do this to you, love. I just can't. I love you too much and I can't see you hurt. Oh I wish to god that we'd met before I married that bitch,'

'David, you mustn't say that. She's the mother of your children.'

'Yes and look at them, apart from Hannah they are carbon copies of their mother. She has no interest in me, and even less now that she knows what the future holds.'

'Well, I know what the future holds and I want you.' With that she pulled me round, put her arms around my neck and kissed me. That was good enough for me, except that we were now in the middle of a busy high street.

Chapter 8

The following day we made our first visit to the Alzheimer Centre. Once again it was left to Constance to take me as Phoebe was not going to be involved with a lot of 'loonies'. Anyway, she hadn't got the time, she said.

I remember walking up the steps of the Old Methodist Church to be met by Josephine Best. She was the organiser of the meetings, or get-togethers, as she preferred to call it. I wasn't that bad at the moment so I fully understood what was going on. I remember walking in to the hall, with Constance on my arm, and hearing Josephine announce, 'Listen, everybody. We have new visitors today, Mr. and Mrs Stephens.'

Constance was about to correct her when I tugged her coat to stop her. I rather liked to imagine Constance was my wife.

There was a mix of people in the hall, from the well-off and well dressed, to the opposite end of the economic spectrum; but we all shared the same torment. People were suffering from varying degrees of dementia and every one of their carers had an equally sad tale to tell each other. I really didn't want to stay, but Constance did. She wanted to know what she was going to face. She wanted to know how each person there had coped and, most importantly, what they needed to do to face the future and what help they could count on. The latter seemed in short supply when my condition became worse.

Afterwards, Constance told me she had learned a great deal and would like to go again. I was once again reluctant but went it was really just an excuse to be with her. We

there were many types of dementia and all could

..c in a variety of way; some lasted years and others as little as six weeks.

We talked to several people and were shocked to hear of the things that might happen, violence being one of the common problems.

'He has thrown ornaments at the television, thrown the television through the window,' said one woman. 'He has attacked the milkman, told him to stay away from his wife and then he came in and asked me what I was doing in the house. I told him I was his wife and he just shouted, "You're not my fucking wife. Get out!" and then pushed me out of the house, locking the door behind me. I had to get the police to let me in. He has destroyed so many things of ours, all our memories, photographs, mementos and other memorabilia, throwing them outside saying it was just a plot to take the house away from him.'

Then there was the college lecturer whose little wife, less than five-feet tall, previously a tranquil woman who wouldn't say boo to a goose, who would now suddenly set about anyone like some fishwife, with fists flaying, feet kicking and using the foulest language you could imagine.

Then there was the old doctor who had begun eating like a cannibal, as though he had been starved, snatching the food off everyone's plate and shoving it into his mouth. There were others who had become totally docile, opposite to their previous feisty character, some who wouldn't talk, some who wouldn't stop talking and many carers had become terrified of living with their loved ones.

There were so many who fell into the same category as me, where all I wanted to do was to go back to Pennington's to work or visit my mother or father. But what was more distressing was the number of carers who wanted respite as they could not sleep properly as their sick partners would wander off in the night or get the car out and drive god knows where. Finally, I felt most vulnerable when I heard that some of the carers had begun negotiating for their partners to be taken into care, with one being advised to have their partner sectioned. I really dreaded the thought of that.

The most significant remark that Josephine Best made that has always stayed with me was, 'It's not your loved one that's ill, it may be his or her body but it is no longer them inside. So don't blame your loved one and always remember them as they were, it will give you strength.'

I knew that I was safe in Constance's hands; I really knew everything would be done by her with my best interests at heart, but I dreaded and often thought about what would happen to me if Constance went first. I knew that my bitch of a wife would not do anything to help me. Constance, to my amazement, was not fazed by what we had seen. I, however, was terrified. I couldn't bear the thought of being in such a position as had been described. Each sufferer had their Constance, who was looking after them for better or worse, but it was when I heard from the majority that they were unable to cope much longer and he or her would have to go into a home, even if it was for a short time just to get a little rest, that I felt despair.

From then on Constance and I worked hard on all the pro-grammes we had been given and I did show a considerable improvement. In fact, I had actually been stable for several weeks, and even though I had effectively returned home, I still went to Constance's almost every day as it seemed the only way to keep sane.

We both wanted this to be a permanent situation, but as James had discussed with us on my last check-up, we had been treading in very thin ice. We attended a few more meetings and then decided it would be better if we spent as much time as possible enjoying the last few able years we had left. Constance had to ask Phoebe if it was all right for her to take me away for the weekend. We picked our moment and planned it for a time when Phoebe was having a party and definitely wouldn't want me around.

Constance had dropped me home and told Phoebe that she was going away for two or three days. A disgruntled Phoebe had to accept but later on she noticed me acting strangely and couldn't cope and immediately telephoned Constance, in panic.

'Constance, darling, I can't have him here; it's too embarrassing, can't you take him with you?'

'No, I'm staying in a hotel and David and needs supervision at night. Can't you manage?'

'No dear. Please take him and I'll pay for his accommodation.'

'I'll try and get an adjoining room. I'll organise something,' Constance replied and then Phoebe startled me with her response.

'It won't make any difference; you have done it before after all.'

Did she know we were having an affair and tolerated it just to get rid of me or was she too stupid for her own good? Anyway, it worked. Phoebe paid for the accommodation and we were ready to enjoy a wonderful time.

We set off with me driving to the Lake District. We stayed in a lovely hotel overlooking Lake Windermere and our room had beautiful views of the surrounding hills as well as the lake.

I remember the weather was glorious, especially walking round Ambleside and along to Windermere, following the edge of the lake. We stopped for lunch in Windermere and then took a rowing boat out onto the lake for the rest of the afternoon. I found a very secluded part, which was unusual, at that time of the year, pulled the boat onto the shore, threw down the car rug, which we had sensibly taken with us, and let the Cumbrian sunshine do the rest. I'm sure if it had been in the height of the season we would have been seen and arrested for gross indecency.

Constance rolled on top of me and began kissing me and gently caressing my hair; it was too much to resist. The ground was dry and we pulled the blanket on top of us, and soon we were undressing.

I remember it felt as though everything was in slow motion, her body moving with mine slowly at first as my hands firmly caressed her torso, then she slithered along me as I gripped her tightly, running my hands down her body to her thighs. She began wrapping her legs round me like some giant python. The more I gripped her, the more tightly she wrapped herself round me and we made love.

We stayed in that position until the shadows began to fall and the evening chill began started to make us cold. God it was lovely, neither of us wanted to move and the more the chill came the closer we cuddled. It was Constance who made the first move, so I won; she now had to help to row the boat.

We pushed it out with our last gasps of energy, each taking an oar and both of us trying to row but failing miserably as the boat went round and round in circles, and the more it did the more incapable we were. I'm sure our laughter could be heard all over the lake. Eventually common sense reigned and we arrived back at the jetty where an anxious boatman was pleased to see our return.

It was a long walk for us poor pensioners as we made our way back to the hotel, laughing nearly all the way at what we had done.

'They would think I was a dirty old man if anyone had seen us,' I said chuckling and proud of myself.

'What about me, what would they think of me?' she demanded indignantly.

'Oh, that you were some high class—'

'Don't you dare say that or you'll get a spank. In fact, you'll get one anyway.'

I started to run, keeping her close on my heels, until I began running on the spot. We were behaving like two young kids and it was the best time in my life.

Constance, much to my embarrassment, had warned the hotel of my condition, and after our first little argument I could fully understand why. In fairness to the hotel, she did not want to upset their other guests and so asked if we could have a table for two near the exit.

It was a good job she did, because on the Sunday night I lost it. The surroundings had become strange and I was disorientated. I suddenly yelled for Constance, who of course was in front of me, and started to cry uncontrollably. She came round as though everything was normal, put her arm round my shoulder and took me out of the restaurant and back to our room.

We went back there a few times over the next few months and every time we had the same room and the same table. The staff had become used to us and they also came to help if I was in difficulties. Constance also had them working on my behalf, by asking, 'What's this David?' or 'What's that David?'

That first time, we drove back to my house to be welcomed by Mrs Cripp.

'You're in trouble, David. She thinks you're having an affair with Constance.'

'Between you and me, Mrs Cripp, I wish I was.'

'Don't be silly, David,' interrupted Constance. 'It will cause trouble.'

'I don't care.'

'Well, I do. It will cause trouble not only for you but me too. You would not be able to cope with this sort of thing. We'd better not see each other for a few days, David.'

No, darling, please don't say that. Please, please, please don't,' I begged her. 'I can't manage without you.'

Constance left looking pale and worried and no matter how I tried to reassure her, she was very concerned.

'Don't worry, David, but I must go now. I'll ring you tonight.'

I went into the lounge whilst Mrs Cripp made me a cup of tea and a sandwich. I sat there just looking into space worrying myself silly, so much so all the good my break had done for me simply evaporated and I soon became a lost soul.

Phoebe arrived back some two hours later with some of her

friends, and with her attitude I'm sure I would have been in for it, but I was on fullers.

'Oh god, look at him. This is what I have to put up with all the time. He can't do anything for himself, he talks gibberish most of the time, his manners are atrocious, and it's driving me mad.'

'Why don't you put him in a home?' one of her friends said.

'I would love to, but it's not that easy because there a few occasions when he is all right and then he would just walk out.'

'Phoebe darling, you are an angel; I don't know how you cope. I thought that Mrs Redpath helped you.'

'She does but really she's useless. She will only take him when she wants to and not when I want to. Like now! Who wants a lunatic walking round the place spoiling everything?'

'Darling, we know how you must feel. He should be put in a home and left there. You can't go on like this.'

I sat in the lounge listening to everything those parasites were saying. None of them had any sympathy for me and the condition I was in. Like Phoebe, they were all for getting rid of me.

It was a difficult situation, unofficially Constance had taken over the mantle of being my carer, but it was beginning to appear to everyone that she was becoming more than just that. I couldn't help the way I felt and neither could Constance and it would have been silly to spoil things by going over the top. Phoebe could have made things very difficult for us and could have embroiled Constance in a Divorce, even though she wanted me out of the way.

It was now spring and the outside entertainment was beginning all over again and of course most took place at the weekend, so it was expedient that I should be taken away and the Lake District became my and Constance's second home.

It was a wonderful spring and I remember saying to myself, if it all ended now I have had the best of times. The sarcastic remark from Phoebe and the quiet words from Mrs Cripp had really made us wary though, so I decided to have a word with James.

As all good friends do, they will look after your best interests and James certainly looked after me. He had discussed my plight with an eminent legal person and had come to the conclusion that should Constance and I continue to live together we could lose all we had so carefully arranged. Phoebe could gain almost everything from a divorce situation. I could lose my full-time nursing at home and as I had not yet survived the necessary seven years after I had gifted various things, these could also be called into question. In fact, for the next two years I had everything to lose; my only consolation was that I could live in peace with Constance and she saw my welfare as paramount, so the matter ended there.

I think it was only because of her fear of having me around that Phoebe put up with the situation and perhaps that overrode the deviousness in her.

I had been full-time with Constance after the last attack for almost two weeks, and after the discussion with James it was time for my return home. She phoned Phoebe with me listening in on the extension. I remember the conversation so well.

Mrs Cripp answered the phone. 'Hello, Mrs Stephens' Residence.' That annoyed me and I couldn't help it, I snapped: 'Whose residence?'

'Sorry, Mr David, Mrs Stephens told—'

'Never mind that, just get my wife.'

We waited for several minutes before she deigned to come to the phone.

'What do *you* want?' she asked rudely.

'It's me, Constance,'

'Constance darling, how are you?' Phoebe's manner immediately changed.

'I'm fine, but so is David, he's ready to come home. He has improved greatly.'

'Are you sure? Wouldn't he be better off in a home, where he can get help all the time?'

'No, no. He's fine. We'll be there in half an hour. 'Bye, see you soon.' And with that Constance put the phone down before Phoebe could respond.

That phone call I remember made me so angry and more determined to fight than anything I had done for years. How dare she take control of the house like that! All she ever wanted was to get me out of the way with my illness or not, but now I was feeling well enough to take her on. At least that was what I was telling myself.

'Come on, David, let's go. Everything will be all right and I know it won't be long before you are back with me. Anyway we'll see each other every day as usual.'

I remember feeling very uncomfortable as we drove up the drive to the front door. I didn't want to be parted from Constance and the security she gave me, but it was taken out of my hands as Mrs. Cripps had seen us arrive and had come to open the door. She was obviously very worried, as her opening remarks confirmed.

'David, I am sorry about the phone call.'

'Don't be silly, we all know what Phoebe's like. Don't you worry, OK?'

'Yes . . . thank you. Do you feel any better? I've missed you, David.'

'Much better, thanks to Constance here. Come on, let's get inside.' And with that we all made our way into the hall. Phoebe had to make her grand gesture by walking down the stairs to meet us in the hall, like some nineteen twenties' dowager.

'Hello Constance, fed up with him are you?'

'Phoebe, don't be so fucking rude and get one thing straight, if you want to go on living here you better be careful what you say. Do you bloody well understand?'

I didn't know where this outburst was coming from, but it worked, she was astonished and unable to respond.

We stood in the hall while she composed herself and seeing me becoming more annoyed and beginning to push passed her, she deigned to open her mouth.

'You'd better come in,' she said, inviting Constance into the lounge, whilst I went to my room to take up my few belongings. I couldn't hear everything they talked about, but I did hear Constance remark, 'I don't mind looking after him, and he's no trouble at all. Anyway, he's company for me and it gives me something to do.'

I entered the lounge to deathly silence. Phoebe obviously did not want me to be part of any arrangements and it was only when Constance brought me into the conversation that I was allowed to talk.

'I was just telling Phoebe how well you are doing, David.'

For the first time for ages I was nearly one hundred per cent OK and able to take part properly in the discussions and it was decided that I should go to Constance's during the day and sleep at home. I didn't like the way Phoebe was manipulating us and that we were allowing it only because of our desire to be together. However, I thought it better, safer in fact, if she drew up a contract. This threw Phoebe, she hadn't a clue what it should say, but in any event, from then on Constance was to be my legal carer, and the only downside was that she was to be employed by Phoebe, with all the disadvantages that entailed, and after that she would simply comment that Patients would often fall for their nurses and then snap "Anyway he's useless in that direction." Little did she know.

I remember Phoebe had been hurried into this situation, by the busy tongues of friends and acquaintances. With the insinuations on the one hand that Constance and I were in more than a carer-patient relationship and on the other hand her desperate need to get rid of me as quickly as possible. She chose the latter.

It worked well for several months and amazingly the deterioration in my condition was hardly measurable. We were congratulated by everyone and Constance in particular for her efforts. We did have my nightly stopovers whenever Phoebe was entertaining, which made it more exciting for both of us as we imagined we were having an illicit affair. Which, of course, we were, but it was with the approval of the third party.

I think it was when Constance went into hospital for a couple of days that I had the first real incident for many weeks. I had to remain at home with the obvious consequences that that had. I was made to feel I was in the way. I drove to the hospital to see my best friend, pretending that I was her husband, and actually stayed with her most of the day and then made my way home, but I never got there. I went to see my mother.

I remember steering the car up the drive, getting out of the car, walking to the door, being greeted by some total strangers and wondering what the hell they had done with my mother.

'What are you doing in my mother's house?' I yelled.

'Hello, David. Your mother died and we bought the house. You remember.' Phillip Russell, the new owner replied. 'Come on in.'

They could see I had lost it and at least they were kind and knowing my home address rang Phoebe, who by this time was in full flow with her bridge friends.

'God, not again,' I heard her shout down the phone. 'I'll send someone to pick him up.'

'But his car is here.'

'Well, it will have to stay there until morning,' she snapped and with that put the phone down.

Twenty minutes later, a very embarrassed couple said good night as the taxi took me back home.

Mrs Cripp answered the door. 'Come on in, Mr David. Go into the lounge and I'll bring you a cup of tea.'

Well, that was that, I couldn't find my way to the lounge, I went everywhere, even into the lounge but didn't recognise it, so I went back into the hall and just waited. Thank goodness Mrs

Cripp was on the ball and sympathetic as she took hold of my hand, with the tray in the other, and led me back to the lounge.

'Come on, Mr David, drink the cup of tea.'

Now, where was I? I seem to forget everything that I have just done and yet I can remember things from way back. God what was I thinking about? Oh yes.

It was about this time on one of our routine visits to James, our doctor, that he told Constance to make sure that Phoebe was kept informed at all times as to my well-being, not only what we were doing but also where we were going.

'I know she hasn't any real interest in you, David, but I think should she decide to become really awkward it would make things very difficult for you and Constance. I for one would not want to see that happen but whatever we might think, Phoebe does have the responsibility, in legal terms, for any decisions that have to be made.'

This set me off, I had one of the worst attacks I had had and it lasted over twenty minutes. I picked up my chair and threw it at some of the equipment; I couldn't speak but simply made a noise, 'Aaaaaaarh.' James's nurse came running in, disturbed by my screams and the crash as the chair knocked most things over.

I began crying uncontrollably until Constance managed to calm me down, which took about five minutes, and after which my brain would not allow me to take responsibility for what I had done. In fact, I remember I simply said, 'Good lord, James, what on earth has happened here?'

I also remember both Constance and James were smiling – no, almost laughing – at the situation, that I could stand there and act so innocent. Thank god for real friends that understood my circumstances. There was no 'you stupid idiot' or worse. It was simply a case of both trying to help me. When I did come round and Constance told me what I had done, I felt dreadful and insisted I pay for the damage. However, the main purpose of the appointment was not lost and we did keep Phoebe informed on all matters, which did make things easier for all concerned. It was now clear though that my biggest problem was that I didn't know how bad I was, because I couldn't remember what I had done and even when I was told, it didn't always register.

The months seemed to fly by and for many of them things were almost normal, which was amazing when I think about it. Apart from my frequent forgetting and perhaps the odd visit to the office to do some work, where I was becoming a bit of a nuisance, but tolerated by the MD and Hannah, as I was comparatively normal. They had even kept my office where I could while away a few hours to give both Constance and Phoebe a break from me. Constance actually encouraged me to go. I remember about this time, I began to get a little worried about Hannah, as she seemed to be working really hard, putting everything into her job and the last thing I wanted was for to have no other life, as I did. But I couldn't persuade her to do otherwise

I was finding if I got upset it would nearly always bring a bad attack on. It could mean either that I would be lost in a world of my own or I could become violent, but it was always disturbing behaviour that I hadn't exhibited in my previous life.

Phoebe would snap at me for just wandering around and getting in the way and I would snap back and that would start me off. Well, I can't pretend I really loved my wife and I'm sure right from the beginning that this was so, but in all my life I have never knowingly been cruel to anyone, in particular to her. But I remember I had gone back to wandering around and had been in the garden just pottering, enjoying the conversation with Chris the handyman cum gardener, when I found myself walking back into the lounge and saw Phoebe.

'What the fuck are you doing in here?' I shouted. That wasn't me shouting, was it? I don't swear.

Phoebe looked at me in stark amazement and replied, 'I live here.'

I was at it again. 'No you bloody don't, get out before I get Chris to throw you out.'

'David, I live here, I'm your wife,' she replied, still in shock.

'No, you're not, I wouldn't marry a sour-faced old cow like you,' I shouted again, moving over to her with my hand raised to hit her, but this time attracting the attention of Chris, who came running in.

'Is everything OK?' he asked, but I had returned to normal the moment I heard his voice, even though I didn't know what had happened.

'Did you hear him, Chris, the way he spoke to me and the way he tried to hit me?'

Thankfully he hadn't seen any violence, saying he had only heard the shouting and wondered if everything was in order.

I now realised what I had done but I could not express my sorrow, it just would not come out and it was so very strange and a new situation for me. I decided to visit James again taking Constance with me and tell him what had happened. On this occasion I could express myself clearly and told him everything.

'I didn't mean to do it and I really wouldn't want to harm her, it just happened.'

'David, it is a symptom of the disease. Some people become totally calm, others violent, and others obtuse; there are so many aspects which take over the individual's character and sometimes there can be a combination of any of these or all of them. We do not know as yet what the triggers are, but I'm sure we are not far away. David, Constance here will help you.'

'Of course I will,' she said, squeezing my hand.

'Try and get him away from Phoebe for a day or so,' said James, 'it will do you both good and it is important to keep taking pills.'

'He will, don't worry,' said Constance.

I remember leaving the surgery wondering what the hell was going to happen to me and which way my disease would show itself. I hated the thought of being nasty to Constance. I wasn't bothered about be horrid to the Dragon, but Constance was special.

I was dropped off at home but as Phoebe was out, I was welcomed by Mrs Cripp.

'Hello, you must be the new house keeper,' I said confidently. 'I'm David.'

'I'm Mrs Cripp, Mr, David. I've been here a long time.'

'Of course you have, I'm sorry. I don't know whether I'm on this earth or Fullers these days.'

'Come on in. Mrs Stephens is out all day today.'

'Thank god for that,' I added unashamedly, causing her to smile.

'Would you like a cup of tea and something to eat?'

'Just a cup of tea and then I'll go out. Thanks.'

Mrs Cripp always did show a great deal of understanding towards me, for which I am very grateful, She would often come and rescue me when Phoebe was having a go, or trying to get rid of me. I spent the most relaxing and least stressful times in my own home in the kitchen with her.

Anyway, I remember after a quick phone call I was away in the car to see Constance. I could still, thankfully, find my way there. I arrived and received the usual lovely warm welcome but also a telling-off as Constance was worried what Phoebe might think, especially after the doctor's warning.

'She's gone out for the day. Shopping I suppose.'

'Good. Well, come on in.' It was the thought of those welcome hugs and kisses that kept me going day after day. I loved them. They were so warm and meaningful; I never wanted them to stop.

We decided to visit Skipton and then go on to Harrogate for

lunch, and we set off with me driving. We had had the most appalling weather recently and as usual the fields on the way were flooded, just showing what the River Aire could do if it wanted to. After a wander round Skipton, we continued on our way to Harrogate. I remember walking into Rackham's, where we planned to have lunch, with Constance on my arm looking and behaving like a woman in love, when who should we bump in to but Phoebe. She had seen us but only seconds after Constance had whispered, 'Phoebe', the latter being with several of her friends. I remember, Constance gripped me tight in embarrassment and I went into one of my turns, which Constance immediately twigged was pretence. It was that soul mate situation when you know exactly what each other is thinking.

'Hello, Phoebe, I thought I would give David an afternoon out but I am having great difficulty at the moment. Could you spare a minute or two? I would like to sit him down in the restaurant but I can't get him up stairs.'

'No, Constance, I'm sorry, but I'm with some people. Take him up in the lift. I'm sure you will be able to cope.'

'Come on, David, let's go.' Constance said, showing her annoyance

We actually heard the old witch say to her friends, 'It's no use having a nurse and having to do it yourself is it?'

'We did it, darling. No harm done,' Constance said as the lift doors opened. We walked in waited for them to close before I took her into my arms and kissed her, only stopping seconds before the doors opened on the first floor. Three people entered and spoiled the next part of the journey but the gripping of my hand, the cheeky knowing smiles and the sexy wink behind their backs told me she would have made love to me there and then, had we been on our own. I just wanted to race back to her home to resume, but some lunch in the restaurant had to do.

I knew we would not be disturbed by the Dragon as she would not want to be involved with me in any embarrassing condition so at least we had a pleasant afternoon.

Chapter 9

Life went on in much the same way for a couple of years, although I was getting slowly worse and my dependence on Constance became much stronger. She had without doubt given me those extra years of fairly normal life with her efforts to keep me going. The constant brain tests, asking me what we had done that day, even carrying on our sexual relationship, played a great part in this process. She put up with such a lot and never grumbled, but it was inevitable that my health would deteriorate further.

Oh, I nearly forgot that we had made several visits to France where we both felt secure and at peace, but in every case it was a clandestine situation. I am sure Phoebe knew I was going with Constance, but we never told her. I remember it was on one of these visits I decided not to fly but I would drive the Seraph. I hadn't driven it much as we had always used Constance's car, as it was more economical. Although I had plenty of money, she had always been careful and not wasted anything; but this time I wanted to go in my lovely Rolls-Royce. I was lucky I could afford such luxury and this car was one of the last made by Rolls-Royce before it was taken over, so very special. It was well known around the area as it had a distinctive number plate PEN 100.

I picked Constance up from her home and we set off down the A1 stopping at Boundary Mills for something to eat and a look round the shop before carrying on to Dover.

We took the ferry stopping at my favourite hotel, The Metropol, in Calais, where we put the car into the garage and were greeted by Philip the proprietor and his staff Catherine, Patrick, Dorothy and Ludivin as though we were long lost friends. They had actually been worrying about us as we had not been there for three months. It was always wonderful arriving there, especially as all my troubles and worries seemed to disappear immediately and I always felt better. Constance also felt these good vibes, which I seemed to exude, and she too felt her cares go away. I should have moved to France as the French were always kind to me.

We unpacked our overnight bags and wandered into the town to get something to eat. I suppose it becomes habit, but I took her to a little bistro called the Brasserie de la Tour for a couple of Kronenburg 1664s and a Calais sole.

Gosh, my mouth's watering just thinking about it. Oh God, I've forgotten where I was. Think man . . . ah yes, at the Brasserie in Calais.

We were sitting round the corner out of the way when I saw in the reflection of a wall mirror none other than Janice and Michael Waterman. Janice was one of Phoebe's best friends. They were looking at the menu on the wall outside and were contemplating coming in.

'Don't look now, but I think we're going to have company,' I remarked. 'It's the bloody Watermans.'

Constance was petrified of being seen, and almost went into shock.

'Don't worry, we'll play it by ear; just carry on as we were and wait and see what happens. If they come over here then we'll laugh with them. But let's hope they don't.'

My hopes were dashed as I saw them walk in, but they sat down in another part of the restaurant and neither of us could see one another.

We decided we would stay put until they had left, but then I noticed we were sitting on the route to the toilet, so we now had to pray they didn't drink too much. When anyone passed it made our hearts skip a beat.

We were beginning to see the funny side of it all by the time the waiter came to take our order. Thank goodness I ordered sole as this took half an hour to cook, which meant we would in the restaurant well over the hour and hopefully the Watermans would have gone by then.

I remembered an incident when I was a young man and told Constance how Gloria Fenston had disappeared under the table. We had a laugh and from that moment on we didn't care who saw us and thankfully we saw the Watermans leave and were able to relax and enjoy the rest of the evening and the meal.

We were both a bit tipsy when we left and returned to the hotel where we had a good night's sleep in our usual room, 106

It was well after midday the following day before we left Calais, having bought some provisions from the patisserie, Chez Fred. Their cakes and gateaux are second to none and make wonderful eating on the autoroutes.

We decided to stop at the Novotel at Rheims. In fact I remember we'd booked the room as they are often busy due to the endless conferences and exhibitions that are held in Rheims.

After settling into our room I remember walking to the car and to my horror there was another English car parked next to mine. I went back in and passing reception I was called by the receptionist: 'Mr Stephens a Mr Waterman has been asking for you.'

He had recognised my car registration number.

'I don't want to see him. Can you tell him I am at a conference and I will contact him later?'

They obliged but Constance and I spent the entire evening looking over our shoulders trying to avoid detection. It was stupid really, as the Watermans knew how Phoebe was with me, so I suppose it wouldn't have mattered.

We rose early, chanced breakfast and then sped south, stopping at Charnay in Beaujolais, to pick up some wine from the local *vignerons*, Jean Louis & Ghislaine Large. They had won several gold medals for their wines and it certainly told. I always loved to buy it there and was greeted as a friend.

We arrived at the house late evening, too tired for anything other than cuddling up in bed. After a good sleep we were woken by the sunshine entering the room and bringing with it a glorious two weeks.

I remember it didn't end there with the Watermans as I saw them in St Tropez but thankfully I saw them first. What was more fortuitous was that I saw Sophie Laveau our neighbour. She was a sexy woman and always made a fuss of me, so told Constance to wait in a nearby shop and made a beeline to Sophie.

'David, darling,' she began and then continued in rapid French telling me how much she had missed me and I made sure the Watermans saw me, which they did, eager to greet me and find out who the woman was.

They were full of it. 'We saw you in Rheims; I'd recognise that car anywhere. Was the conference good?'

'Conference?' Then it dawned. 'Oh the one in Rheims, yes not bad. Good bit of business to come from it.'

'Aren't you going to introduce us then?' Janice asked.

'Of course, Sophie this is Janice and this is Michael Waterman. Sophie is my mistress, aren't you Sophie dear?'

'You are naughty,' she said in her tantalising sexy French accent, which was enough to send Janice in a spin. I'm sure they couldn't get back to England quick enough, as they certainly left us quickly, especially when Sophie began shaking her body and going, 'Ooooooh.'

Constance had watched everything and I remember her being a little jealous at Sophie's antics, but at least it gave us something to laugh about and we didn't see the Watermans again.

I didn't know at the time but it was to be one of my final visits to my second home, certainly the last where I was a least operating at nearly full capacity. Although I had been taking the pills and doing everything that had been recommended, I was nevertheless losing it little by little.

We had two wonderful weeks in each other's company and wanted nothing else. I can't honestly say I wasn't one hundred per cent all the time, as I did have some difficult moments, like getting lost, shouting for Constance, even forgetting where I was in the house and wandering off to see my dad, but we coped with that. It was when the time arrived to go back to England that things began to get really difficult and I started to worry about the dreadful things that awaited, especially once I had dropped Constance off at her home and was alone. That was how I saw myself as I slowly made my way back to Phoebe's.

Why I keep thinking that, I will never know. It wasn't Phoebe's home, it was mine as well. I lived there. It was my address, but I still think of it as hers.

It was the usual, normal welcome home.

'You've decided to come back have you? And what about Sophie?'

I just laughed. 'I knew that silly woman would tell you. It was Sophie Laveau and you know what she's like.'

I continued laughing as I went to my room. It was the same old story, the moment I was with Phoebe the stress would start and I began to lose control. I just swore and told her to piss off, much to the amusement of Mrs Cripp who had come to welcome me home and to offer me a cup of tea.

It's funny but now I do remember my last visit to France. It was a disaster, but it started well enough. I decided I wanted to go to France for an extended holiday, four or five weeks and we thought we should give Phoebe the opportunity to refuse, which she did, whispering to Constance, 'If you want me to spend four weeks with that imbecile you must be off your head.'

111

Constance was furious at the remark and laid into her with the result that Phoebe snapped back: 'If you want to take him, you take him. I want nothing to do with it.'

This was just what we wanted as it would get me away from the stress of home and the double life I led, and perhaps it might enable my condition to remain stable. I did check with my specialist and James that we had everything we needed and we flew from Manchester to Nice, hiring a car when we got there.

But I got lost in the gents' toilet at Manchester airport and couldn't get out. I began shouting for Constance, which embarrassed every male in the toilet and more so when she had to come in and get me, as I would not go out with anyone else.

I think the entire airport heard my shouts and, of course, I was the centre of attraction when I was rescued. However, I remember that when I did get out, I hadn't been to the toilet and now wanted to go. Constance would not risk it happening again and took me into the ladies and waited outside the cubicle door for me.

When we were getting on the plane, I thought it was a train and asked the hostess, 'What's the next stop?'

'Nice,' she replied.

'But I don't want to go to Nice. I'm going to La Croix Valmer.'

'Don't worry, darling,' Constance reassured me, 'you'll be all right, you're with me. We have to go to Nice first to get to La Croix.'

'But I don't want to go to Nice.'

'Come on, David, I've got you.' She held me by the arm and gently took me to my seat where I was next to the window with Constance sat next to me.

I suppose we were in the plane for a good hour before it taxied along the runway and I started to panic.

'It's going too fast, the train's going too fast,' I said loudly, causing the stewardess to come along and see what the problem was. Constance explained my situation and she at least was satisfied. As for me, I simply closed my eyes and held her hand in the hope it would all end quickly.

I had flown dozens of times before and never been concerned, but this time I was terrified. I did not open my eyes until the plane had stopped and Constance was pulling at me to go with her. She had to treat me like a child as I really was confused.

I remember when we entered the arrivals hall, I was still thinking it was the railway station and asked the enquiry desk, which was the platform for La Croix Valmer. Naturally, when Constance explained I was a little confused they understood. We collected the car but there was no way I could drive whilst in this condition. Constance once again she had the job of getting us there, talking to me all the time to keep me amused, so I wouldn't be too much trouble. But then at the *peage* she dropped her credit card outside the car as she tried to push it into the machine and I thought she was going to leave me.

All this and it was only the first day. By the time we had driven the sixty miles home, she was worn out.

I began to come round by the early evening and we chanced a visit to La Mise à L'eau, my favourite restaurant, which as usual was wonderful. Claudie and Gerard were so pleased to see us. I did, however, hear Constance say I was getting worse which upset me, not because Constance had told other people but because I realised I was obviously much worse for her to have said something.

I was OK for the first week or so and things were almost back to normal where at least Constance could cope, but then it happened: I went walk about.

I had set off late evening when Constance was in the bath, got dressed and walked out of the house and wandered off. I don't know how I did it, but I was found the following day wandering in Toulon. I looked wretched when I was taken to the police station by some kind old lady, where I was asked all sorts of questions and couldn't answer one of them; but then to my utter astonishment, they found our address and phone number in La Croix which Constance had sewn into my coat and jacket.

The police drove me home to a very ashamed and embarrassed

Constance as they had had the local police out looking for me, with loudspeakers asking in both French and English if anyone had seen me. She was never cross with me, in fact she apologised for not looking after me properly, but when the realisation of what I had done did get through to me I too was ashamed.

It would appear I caught a bus and the driver saw that I wasn't behaving normally and let me off in Toulon without paying. However, he hadn't the sense to tell someone, especially as I was in my slippers and had no money.

It wouldn't have been so bad but I did the same thing a few days later, only this time I walked up to Les Hauts de Peynie to the very spot Constance and I had gone to on our first time together and wasn't found for two days. Once again the loud-speakers were out but no one had heard or seen anything, until the police were informed by a local man that he had seen someone of my description walking up to Les Hauts. The police telephoned Constance to tell her there had been a sighting and the moment she heard where it was, she knew I would be at our spot. She told the police of her idea and sure enough I was found there cold and miserable. One again I felt terrible when I knew what trouble I had caused, but even more so when I heard what the police wanted to do.

They felt it would be better if I were locked up for my own protection. Constance promised that it would not happen again but I was effectively locked away at night so that I couldn't get out.

During one of my better moments when I was compos mentis, we discussed the situation we were in and Constance now felt we would be unable to visit France again. I knew it was the right decision, but anybody who understood what the French house meant to me would also realise how difficult it was for me to accept the decision.

I had always been at peace in La Croix. I had many friends that I got on well with and they all accepted me for what I was as I accepted them just as they were. It was a world I had loved.

We decided to go home earlier and that we would spend the last week saying goodbye to all our friends. Firstly, it was Simone our housekeeper and her husband Roger, then Daniel and Marie Ange, Josie and her mother and Bernard and Janet our neighbours where we had spent many an evening in wonderful company and having delicious meals. At Daniel's it was always a meal from a different part of France, at Bernard's it was always provençale, at Josie's it was always a party and included her special friends, some bohemian, some well to do, but all full of life, infected by Josie's *joie de vivre*.

Oh god, I do miss these friends. I just wish I could have grown old with them and faded as they would and not as I have.

To tell them that this was the last time was a dreadful experience, even though I knew they understood the reasons. I have never shed so many tears in my life, which were reciprocated by all my friends. It was as though I was going home to die; I was not however fortunate in that matter; death would have been easier.

I have missed my restaurant La Mise à L'eau having spent many happy hours in that place. I remember the wonderful gambas with aioli every Friday; the *vin de table* which was always good, whether it be red or rosé. The last meal was of course gratuité, but it was the hugs, squeezes and kisses as we left the place for the last time which were heart wrenching. It was very sad but we knew it had to be done; we couldn't risk any more episodes.

'David what's the matter, you're crying again? Come on, I don't like to see you like this. Tell me what the matter is.'

I tried to utter the words, 'my home in France', but I'm not sure whether or not they came out. However, Sister sat on my bed, took my hand in hers and said,, 'Don't worry, everything will be all right.'

But I did worry and knew that nothing would be all right again. I missed my home in France. It was where I had spent the happiest times of my life. No one could understand the way I felt about my little part of France and the time I spent there with Constance.

I remember those walks along the old Chemin de Feu to the village. In January and February it would be like a tunnel of yellow as the mimosa was out in full flower.

In May and June the wild flowers would be filling the banks of the old railway line, with the bright pale yellow of the dandelions standing tall amongst them. Then there were the blues of the vinca and other flowers with their different shades to match, followed by the first of the bright red poppies thronging in to make wonderful splash.

The eucalyptus standing tall, looking as though someone has stolen the bark, was almost pale white, delivering that delicious perfume when it rained, surrounded by pine trees with the occasional cypress standing like Cleopatra's needle amongst them all, as if it had to reach the sun first.

'David what is the matter? You can't go on like this. Come on please try to tell me what's upset you.'

I managed to say, 'I miss France.' And then I continued crying.

The sister was very kind but I had had it; I couldn't stop thinking about it. The more she tried to take my mind off things with the several cups of tea, the more I went back to my memories of France.

I know this would sound daft to anyone if I told them, and I know I was crying, but I loved thinking about it. I loved to remember all the beautiful things about the place and I was only upset because I loved it so. People would think it silly to upset myself so much. Mind you, they think I'm gaga now, so I suppose it wouldn't make much difference.

'It was wonderful there.'

'What was, David?' the sister asked, a little surprised I had spoken, and even more so when I replied.

'My lovely house in France.'

*

I went back to my thoughts, imagining I was telling Sister how I used to love champagne or Anjou rosé just sitting on my terrace, watching the boats pass by. One day it would be the Clemenceau, the big French aircraft carrier gliding past on its way to Toulon and the naval base, then the next we would see tankers and cargo ships heading for Marseille or Fosse sur Mer and in the morning, the little flotillas of small yachts as the sailing school would be holding lessons for the children from all age groups. The teachers would be gliding round them on a high-speed dinghy just in case one got into trouble and always we would see the big yachts, property of the millionaires who inhabit Gods lovely acre.

The sun would go down and we would see those magical colours shimmering across the calm blue sea, disturbed only by the massive cruise liners gently passing, like some giant Christmas tree, fully bedecked in lights.

Oh god it reminds me of my friend Juliette and her husband Michel, the retired postman. He was an incredibly strong swimmer and would walk into the sea and swim out of sight. Sometimes it was over an hour before he came back.

'Where have you been Michel?' my son William would ask.

'Africa,' he would reply and then every Sunday he would cycle a hundred kilometres along with every other self-respecting Frenchman.

But it was Juliette who I loved. She was a lovely tiny lady – only about 4 feet 8 inches high; very simple, nothing pretentious or over the top with her, except for their lovely house overlooking the bay of Cavalaire, and set in its beautiful garden complete with swimming pool.

She hadn't read the paper telling her that there was to be a re-enactment of the landings on the beach of Cavalaire to celebrate the 50th anniversary of the 1944 battle during the Second World War. Over 20,000 men and machines were to be landed between 5 a.m. and nightfall.

At 6 a.m. she was driving to Cavalaire and was stopped by an armoured personnel carrier and thirty or so armed men covered in war paint and camouflage. She was so terrified she got out of her car with her hands up and surrendered. They had to take her to the medical orderlies to give her a drink to help her recover from the shock.

I remember the journey back to England that last time. I hated every second of it and when we arrived home, I was feeling terribly depressed and even more tired than I had before we went. Thank god we went to stay at Constance's that first night; had it been at Phoebe's I think I may have done her some harm had she started on me.

Chapter 10

The following day I had a real relapse not only did I go wandering off, looking for the village in France, but after being brought home by a kind person who found me, I was lambasted by Phoebe for causing her grief.

Then I said, 'I don't know who this stupid cow is. Get the police and get her out of my house.'

Once again the dear old Mrs Cripp came to the rescue and told my rescuer the real story.

I remember the only good thing that happened that year Hannah had a little girl Elizabeth and from the beginning they called her Betty, which always upset me as why give her such a lovely name and not use it. I had really been worried that she would not have children as her life, as mine was wrapped up in Pennington's and she was almost forty. It was lovely to see her grow up and it gave me a new lease of life.

Things were always bad at home and in particular when it was the summer outdoor season when Phoebe liked to hold garden parties. I was always shipped off to either act as drinks orderly or ushered into the lounge or study out of the way – and that was even before I was ill. But after I became difficult I was banished to my room. Sometimes, however, I found my way outside, only to be humoured by Phoebe's friends who always made the same sort of comment: 'Oh, she's allowed you out has she, David?'

I would put up with it for the sake of peace and quiet. However, I remember one lovely afternoon in June when

Phoebe's bridge club was celebrating winning the league title. It wasn't really a big thing but Phoebe wanted to impress all her friends so invited a hundred guests. Constance was included, but only to keep me in check. We were to have a buffet and there were three or four long tables laid out with a wonderful array of meats, fish, salads, sweets – you name it, and it was there. There was also, of course, a constant supply of champagne, other wines and spirits; she had even arranged for a three-piece band to play with an area of the lawn boarded to enable dancing to take place. I had to hand it to her, she could organise a good party, but never out of her allowance.

The guests had arrived, the band was playing and everyone was enjoying themselves – until the speeches began. The president of the bridge club thanked Phoebe and me for the wonderful party and then began the presentations to the various players. I was simply walking past the drinks table when I tripped over the electricity cable and went flying, causing everything to crash to the floor. It was a disaster and Phoebe just lost it.

'Constance,' she yelled above the noise. 'Take this bloody imbecile away.'

Constance came running over and snapped: 'David is not a bloody imbecile. Come on, David, let's get you home.' She put her arm around me and walked me out of the garden and into the house. Even the Dragon realised she had gone too far, simply by looking at the faces of all those who heard what she'd said, which was probably everyone. Embarrassed, she followed us into the lounge, pretending to be concerned; however, the moment she thought we were out of earshot she laced into Constance.

'How dare you talk to me like that in front of people, and in particular in front of my friends? I no longer want you to help me with David – in fact, you can leave now.'

'Don't be silly, Phoebe. You have no control of this situation, I was employed to do a job and I will do it. You, my dear, can go to hell and if you want to make anything of it, I promise you will regret it. You are cruel, wicked, uncaring, selfish and the most evil woman I have ever had the misfortune to meet. And you won't stop me helping David because he hasn't got a wife that cares about him and he needs me. It's a wonder you have any friends at all, the way you behave.'

'We'll see about that,' Phoebe stammered, leaving the room visibly shaken.

'Sorry about that,' she shouted above the noise, as she resumed her role in the garden.

The embarrassed silence changed to an embarrassed chatter with a few remarking that they wouldn't put up with what Phoebe has to, and that I should be locked up where I couldn't do any harm. It always astonished me that people can be so insensitive about others' misfortune and even as I was, I wouldn't have wished my disease on any of them.

I remember we left the house and went to Constance's, where I seemed to be in shock. I had lost it badly and for the first time couldn't remember who Constance was.

'Let's get you inside, David,' she said opening my car door.

'Where am I? And who are you?' I asked. I could see the glimmer of shock in her face as she struggled to not to get upset. 'I'm Constance, David, your best friend and you're staying with me for a few hours.'

'No, I'm not and I don't live here. I am going back home, to Constance, where I'm wanted. You're just an imposter'

'Please, David, come on in,' she said, almost pleading.

'I've told you,' I began shouting, 'I am bloody well going home. Give me the keys to the fucking car or I'll fucking walk.'

'I'll take you,' Constance replied, now becoming visibly distraught. I had never sworn at her before and although I could hear myself say the foul words, I couldn't do anything to stop myself; the words just came out.

'I'll take my fucking self. Give me the keys,' I shouted at the top of my voice.

'David, please let me take you. You are so angry you are not in a fit state to drive.'

We spent the next minute or so verbally fencing until I became so angry she gave me the keys and within seconds I was in the driver's seat and away. Hannah told me later that Constance had telephoned Phoebe and blasted her, telling her she had caused no end of damage to my welfare and had set me back months.

At that time though, Phoebe wouldn't come to the phone so she had to tell Mrs Cripp that I was on my way back in her car and that she could not be responsible for my behaviour.

It really was poetic justice. Somehow I found my way back home and to everyone's surprise I re-joined the party.

'Constance, what are all these people doing here? Get rid of them,' I said.

'They're our guests and keep your voice down,' Phoebe stammered, becoming very embarrassed.

'Constance, get rid of them.' I began raising my voice 'They are in MY house and I don't want them here.'

'David for god's sake, keep your voice down and I'm Phoebe not Constance.'

'Of course I know who you are, I've lived with you for years and why are you calling yourself Phoebe?'

I didn't know why I was behaving like this and I couldn't reason with myself. I was also becoming somewhat amorous towards Phoebe, causing her to be more embarrassed, especially when I kept calling her Constance.

'I'm Phoebe,' she answered angrily to one of my questions.

'Don't be silly. I know who you are. You're the cow that I have been married to for forty years'

'Come with me,' I commanded, grabbing her arm and pulling her upstairs. She dared not scream as she did not want this witnessed by the visitors. I managed to get her into her bedroom, shut the door behind us, but failed to lock it. She slipped my hold, jumped over the bed and after a few attempts to get past me succeeded and raced downstairs to with the safety of her guests.

Eventually I got her into the kitchen and began to frighten her when we were interrupted by Josh.

'Leave Mother alone,' he shouted, before going to Phoebe to comfort her. She hugged and kissed him, which prompted me to shout back. 'You've always preferred him to anyone else, haven't you?'

'Yes,' she screamed, 'and he's the only thing I've got that you've had nothing to do with or your bloody family'

I could see that she could have bitten her tongue out and from the terrible reaction that Josh had, I remember I was suddenly brought back to real time and was truly shocked. I walked out of the house, got into the car and drove away. I had no idea where I was going; I just drove and drove until the car ran out of petrol. I had no idea where I was, or what time it was, all I knew was that it was dark and there were no streetlights. I stayed in the car all night and all the following day and night before I was found by some ramblers, who just happened to be passing. They called the police and an ambulance and I was carted off to hospital where thankfully Constance was noted down as my next of kin, as she encouraged me to carry a card for such an event as this.

I was once again a lost soul and could not remember anything that Phoebe had said or I had done, and was placed in the geriatric ward in Glasgow Royal Infirmary, until Constance arrived to take me home. I didn't speak a word to anyone until she did.

'David, we've been worried out of our minds,' she said as she hurried over to hug me.

'We've tried to get him to talk to us, but he just sits there,' the ward sister told her. 'He has had a few hot drinks but he won't eat a thing. I really think he should remain here for a short while, until we see what's wrong with him,' she continued.

'No, I want to go home,' I said, almost whispering my words.

'All right, David, we'll go home,' Constance said, squeezing my hand in reassurance.

We were asked by the hospital to call at the police station to discuss what was to happen about the car, which had been taken to their pound for security reasons. Here, we had the first of our two shocks, firstly the cost of collecting the car and storing it but secondly words which I never wanted to hear: the officer suggested that perhaps I shouldn't be driving. He told us that he would have to contact our local police about it.

The AA took the vehicle back home and I went with Constance and as she had brought my night attire and a change of clothing, thinking I might be kept in hospital, she decided we would have a dirty stop-over, and where did we finish up? Only at our lovely hotel in Windermere.

The mere fact of being with her gave me life; I never wanted to leave her arms, I never wanted to stop holding her. I would watch her lips coming to mine until I could no longer see them and then feel the coolness as they caressed mine. I just wanted to spend the rest of my life lying next to her on our special bed, in our special hotel, away from everything. I slept solidly for almost twenty hours and Constance let me sleep, spending the time sitting quietly on the terrace overlooking the lake.

We spent another night at the hotel before making our way back to my home to be greeted by Phoebe, who was unusually concerned.

'Hello, Constance,' she began, as though she was pleased to see us. 'Is David OK?'

'Yes, but he's a bit shaken and not wholly with it. Are you, David?'

I just smiled and we chatted in generalities for a few minutes as we entered the house and made our way to the lounge.

'Has David mentioned anything about Josh?' Phoebe asked casually.

'No, what about him?' Constance asked.

She looked at me but I had no idea what Phoebe was talking about and just shrugged.

'Oh it doesn't matter,' Phoebe replied.

'Phoebe you will have noticed that David can vividly remember many things that have happened in the past and distant past,'

Constance said, 'but as for the present, he cannot remember anything. That's one of the problems with dementia you know.'

The relief on Phoebe's face showed like some not-guilty verdict and matters were left at that.

Constance returned to her home leaving me to be treated, for the first time, like a human being by Phoebe, who was obviously fishing to see whether I did remember her outburst or not. However, once she was convinced the coast was clear she slowly began to get back to normal.

It was never the same for me after this as shortly afterwards the police arrived at the house to have a chat with Phoebe and me about my condition and, more important from my point of view, about my driving.

'Mr David there's an Inspector Johnson to see you,' Mrs Cripp said, as she invited him into the hall.

'Bring him in here,' I responded, at which Phoebe came hurrying to see what was going on.

'I'm Mrs Stephens,' she said pointedly, now fully back to her normal self. He shook her hand and was invited to sit down.

'What can we do for you?' she asked.

'Well, I've come to see you about your husband's driving.'

'Why? Has he caused an accident?'

'No nothing like that. He was found in a lane, having run out of petrol, total oblivious of anything, and we think he may have been there for two or three days. He had no idea how he got there, how long he had been there or where he had come from. You can imagine what a danger that could be. Thankfully every-thing was all right and no harm was done. But our worry is about the future and whether or not he should be driving at all. It really is not just about what can happen to him – although that is an important point, of course – it is about what harm he can cause to others.'

I was very worried by what I was hearing, but when the Dragon put her oar in I was devastated.

She put the knife in and then turned it. 'I have warned him about this, haven't I, David? He is becoming a danger to himself and to others. I'm always scared when we go out and he wants to drive.' She put her hand on my knee as if to tell the officer she loved me but it was for the best.

You bloody bitch, I thought. I never bloody go out with you. You fucking bloody bitch. I only wish I could have let them hear me, but I just sat there taking it.

'I'm glad you said that, Mrs Stephens. It shows a sense of responsibility. Mr Stephens, I am going to have to revoke your driving licence until you have taken a test. Now, you really must not drive your car as you will not be covered by insurance.'

'I'll make sure he doesn't, officer,' the Dragon said with a smile which said, one nil to me.

'The DVLA will be contacting you about the test. They'll tell you when and where to go to. Thank you for your time,' then, without another word, he was gone

The Dragon didn't waste a minute before picking up the phone to put the boot in.

'Constance, darling, we've just had the police here and they've taken David's driving licence off him. Would you please return his car?'

She had deliberately put the phone on loudspeaker so that I would hear, knowing full well it would distress me.

'It belongs to Pennington's doesn't it?' Constance asked. 'Shall I take it back there?'

'No, bring it here I'll decide what to do with it. I'll use it for a short while; it will be a change from the Range Rover.'

'All right, I'll do that,' Constance said.

'Straight away,' Phoebe added haughtily.

I knew what Constance must be thinking as I had made her the owner of Pennington's and now there was that cow lording it over her.

'I can't at the moment I'm busy,' Constance replied.

'Constance, I said now.'

And with that Constance hung up, leaving Phoebe in an absolute rage.

'Who the hell does she think she is? I will teach her a lesson or two.'

I knew she had not responded in deference to me. I was in enough trouble as it was without her making my life more miserable. One day I thought to myself, one day.

Within a couple of hours Phoebe had gone to Constance's and taken the car. It was my Rolls-Royce Silver Seraph. I loved the car and the thought of her driving it made me angry inside, but I seemed to be in passive mode and could do nothing about it.

However, this did not last long, the mere sight of someone driving my car set me off.

'Get out, that's my car,' I shouted at Phoebe as she drove off down the drive and then stupidly telephoned the police to say she had stolen it and what was worse, I telephoned them several times with the same complaint.

'Right, Mr Stephens, we will get someone on to it straight away,' they said at first. Then it became, 'Thank you, Mr Stephens, we will get her to bring it back straight away. Will that be all right?'

'Yes fine. Make sure you tell her off won't you?'

When she returned I would always say something like, 'I knew they would make you bring it back.'

The following weekend soon came along and of course I was not required. Constance was given her orders not to bring me back before Monday evening as Phoebe was having a party on Sunday which wouldn't finish until late, and then she wanted Monday to recover.

Well, it was nice, but we spent the entire time worrying about the driving test I was going to have to take. I had received the date, but as I was not allowed to drive, I couldn't practice, and what was worse I was not going to be allowed to drive my own car as it was to be one belonging to the test centre.

Constance had the foresight to find out what sort of car it

would be and we hired the same. Pennington's yard became the new test centre. We spent several hours reversing, parking the car between other cars and so on and I remember I wasn't too bad.

The day came and thank god I was on form, especially when the first test to be undertaken was by a psychologist and an examiner. They gave me a letter recognition test, which was a piece of paper with dozens of different letters on it, and I had a few minutes to cross out all the 's's and 'f's. I was very fortunate as this was similar to a test Constance used for me. Then there was another with pictures and one with objects. I passed them all, but only just.

Then came the driving test and I could read the number plate at twenty-five yards and take the car out of a parked area. In one respect I found it difficult to drive as the car was manual and I was used to an automatic, but in another the Ford Escort was much smaller and somewhat easier to drive in town. I was criticised for driving too slowly, particularly on the bypass, but at least I passed. They did, however, protect themselves by ordering another test on my next birthday and I needed a doctor's certificate.

It was a most wonderful feeling to go home, demand the keys from Phoebe and go over to Constance's and crow. The look of disappointment on Phoebe's face was so obvious I thought she would cry.

The euphoria was not to last long though as six months later she succeeded in destroying my life, as on the next test I failed. My mental capacity let me down and my driving skills in a busy town centre were non-existent.

The sad part about this for me was it was the first time in my life I had failed at anything.

Losing the car knocked me for six and I know it took a permanent chunk out of my mental capacity, with the result that things began to deteriorate dramatically, particularly when I was at my home. It seemed that once inside those four walls I became a very different person and Phoebe was the centre of all my change. At first I began to get more violent, throwing things around and I would shout complete filth, calling her the most dreadful things. It was something I had only done once or twice before in short outbursts, but now I was going through a stage when it was most of the time.

There were many times when I couldn't recognise her and threw her out of the house. There were many times when I would call Mrs Cripp and ask for her help with the 'imposter'. The police were frequently being called and I was asked, 'Do you know this woman?'

'Of course I do, it's my wife. We've been married nearly fifty years unfortunately. I don't know what her name is though.'

There were many times when I took her to the police station and complained she was breaking in to the house. But Phoebe was crafty and learning quickly. The moment we walked into the police station, she would complain that I had beaten her up and threatened her and of course each time they made a note of it and it was another nail in my coffin.

Furthermore she never mentioned Constance and it always made it appear it was her who had the sole care.

Finally, on the 14 December, she had waited for a time when she knew I was suffering badly and took me down to the police station where she pleaded for help; only this time I hadn't done anything.

'I was on my own,' she told them. 'The cook was taking the evening off and he started. He grabbed me by the hair and told me if I didn't go with him he would hit me. He's a big man and still very strong and I can't manage him or fight him off.'

'Well, David, what do you have to say for yourself?' the duty sergeant asked.

I was in a daze and couldn't believe what she had done, and at the same time I didn't know how to answer, the words just wouldn't come out.

'I'm going to call for the doctor and let him examine David,' the sergeant said, 'so if you would just come with me and wait a few moments, he will be with us shortly.'

I remember waiting and by now I was totally confused and asking for Constance and another officer was asking who Constance was.

'Oh, she's just a figment of his imagination,' said Phoebe. 'She's his little security blanket. You know children have their teddy bears, well David has his Constance. He's got Alzheimer's and most of the time he doesn't know where he is. He should really be in a home, but I don't want that. We've been married fifty years you know and I don't want to lose him. It would be a big wrench.'

'Oh I see, I understand. It must be difficult for you.'

'Yes, it is, very.'

We waited several more minutes with the officer popping in to see if Phoebe was all right and then the doctor arrived.

'Good evening, Mrs Stephens, I have been briefed by the duty sergeant and he tells me they have seen you regularly both here and at your home and that David is becoming violent and difficult to handle.'

'Yes, I'm sorry to say I haven't had a night's sleep for nearly a week and I'm worn out.'

She's lying, I thought, can't you see she's lying. Don't send me away, please don't send me away. It was no use, the stress had put me into reverse and I could not respond, so much so the doctor didn't even do any tests, he simply phoned for an ambulance and I was taken to hospital.

Phoebe didn't even want to go with me and I was just left on my own. Thank god for James Percival, and what a friend he turned out to be. He actually passed me in a corridor in the hospital and turned to find out what was wrong. The orderlies said I had beaten my wife up and I was to be sectioned as it was happening all the time.

'That's not true,' James said. 'He's my patient and I know him well. Don't worry, David, I'll sort this out.' He squeezed my arm in reassurance.

I was then taken to a ward and for the first time in my life I was locked in and I found my spirit fading. I thought I had lost. The ward itself was lovely and the nurses were very kind, but the inmates – and I considered myself to be one – were in a terrible state. Some were shouting, some were creating mayhem, some were completely docile and lost to the world, and nearly all of us had a vacant look. It was awful and now I was part of this world.

The doctors began to examine me but I became vacant and I fell asleep with exhaustion so things were left until the morning. James was assured that no decisions would be made until he had had chance to investigate matters. He was also surprised that Phoebe hadn't bothered to come with me.

I was to be in no more than two days whilst the doctors examined me and assessed me, but fate took a terrible turn; on the second day the ward contracted a very dangerous bug and none of us were allowed to leave the ward, and worse, none of us were allowed visitors. I became so depressed over the next few days that I began losing my ability to reason and just started to wander. I remember palling up with this old chap and we wandered round the ward just chatting to each other. Hour after hour we were talking and all of it was gibberish and I remember I must have repeated myself at least a hundred times over the eleven days I was in, because I know he did.

I never saw a paper, something I really enjoyed and which kept me in touch with the world and what was going on, but I suppose the others were so far gone they could no longer read and they presumed I was the same. Two of the nurses did recognise that I wasn't loopy all the time and made an effort to talk to me; one even asked me to help with one of the patients and that made me feel a bit better.

Constance often phoned and I remember on one occasion the sister told her not to worry, as I had met a new friend and they were getting on like a house on fire. When I told her he was totally away with the fairies and he was the only inmate I could talk to she became more worried.

The ward reopened on the eleventh day and my first visitors were James and Constance. I could see them through the window as they came from the car park. The mere sight of my two best friends and their smiling, friendly faces seemed to light a spark and enabled me to avoid any further problems. Constance stayed with me until I was allowed back home later in the day. She filled me in with all the news, how James had made extensive enquiries as to what had happened. He had even visited the police station where he eventually spoke to the duty sergeant and the doctor who were on duty that night. Thankfully, he had Constance with him as they were on the way to visit me in hospital, so when the officer remarked, 'He even wanted his teddy bear Constance.'

'Where did you get that from?' James asked.

'His wife told us he needed it all the time.'

'This is Constance and she is his carer and when he is in distress he often calls out for her. Officer, I am sure his wife no longer wants him at home, he is becoming an embarrassment to her; she wants him out of the way and this was one way of doing it.'

'I thought it strange she didn't go with him after she had told us they had been married for nearly fifty years. I have noted your comments, doctor.'

Unfortunately, we did have to wait for Phoebe to arrive as she was the next of kin, and it was almost noon before she deigned to come. She was shocked to find James and Constance waiting for her, along with another doctor and a psychologist.

It wasn't often Phoebe was at a loss for words, but on this occasion she was and was castigated for wasting everybody's time. She was told quite categorically that I was not going to be sectioned and that I was not ready for it. They suggested that I should have a carer that could take more responsibility and it would ease the burden for her.

'He's got one,' she snarled, hating being put in her place.

I went home with James and Constance whilst Phoebe remained with the hospital doctors, no doubt plotting my downfall again.

During the eleven days they had actually worked out what drugs I should be taking and how and when to take them, which did actually make me feel a little brighter, but it meant I was now on a strict regime twenty-four hours a day for life. If it meant a better life for all then what was the hardship? The problem was they were given to Phoebe who was given the instructions on what to do. Naturally she did not inform Constance and it was left to James to organise matters.

Chapter 11

Much to Phoebe's annoyance I was dropped off at home. At least I got a welcome from Mrs Cripp, but then things drifted on much as before with a gradual deterioration in my condition, possibly because Phoebe would forget my tablets and it needed Constance to check on the tablet count and what I had and hadn't taken. It was obvious that my condition worsened when I did not take them so perhaps Phoebe had an ulterior motive.

I had decided to talk over my problems with James, when I was in a coherent state, naturally taking Constance with me. The situation was made more difficult because of my dual residence. We three would have preferred me to stay with Constance, but for all Phoebe's bravado, the comments she made now and again tended to make me believe she was somewhat jealous of Constance' ability to keep me going. I even suggested a divorce, but James felt it would not only make things more difficult for me. He also realised that if Phoebe succeeded in having me sectioned, then both situations could have negated the final will and arrangements I had made. He felt that I should now employ three nurses to be available twenty-four hours a day, which was what I had planned for and which would take the pressure off Phoebe and maybe help the situation.

When I was at Constance's there would be no need for assistance at this time. It was now time to discuss the matter with Phoebe.

James came round to the house at a pre-arranged time to

coincide with Constance taking me home. She left immediately, leaving James to deal with matters.

'Hello, Phoebe, David, I've come to talk to Phoebe about your future requirements. Can we sit down somewhere?' he asked.

'Mrs Cripp, make a pot of tea for us, and don't listen in,' Phoebe said, behaving as she normally did and making us all wince.

'David is going to need full-time nursing very soon and he made arrangements many years ago for the funds to be made available to have twenty-four-hour nursing care at home.'

'I'm not having nurses in my house,' Phoebe shouted, interrupting James. 'He can go to that bloody woman more often, or go into a home.'

'Phoebe I have got to have more assistance and now I need help at home. You are too busy . . . so—'

'No. No.No,' she interrupted. 'I am not having it. Not in my house.'

'Phoebe, it's my house and YOU WILL DO AS YOU'RE BLOODY TOLD,' I shouted, losing my temper.

'Calm down, David, it won't do you any good to get upset,' James interrupted. 'Phoebe, we'll talk about this later on, but he will need help soon.'

'He can go to bloody Redpath's, I'm not having nurses here.'

This was the start of what I remember being one of the worst periods of my life. Ooooh I nearly forgot! My favourite little boy was born Max. That's right Hannah had her second child within a year of Elizabeth. I remember I used to take him out in the push chair, but only in Constance's garden as they couldn't trust me out in the road as I might wander off. Anyway I was pleased because those two little children did love me and I them.

What was I thinking of before I remembered my grandchildren? It was something to do with the nurses. Yes that's it, I did employ two nurses when I was at home, which became an extra day a week as I had to protect Constance from any legal matters that Phoebe might start, even though she didn't want me at home and I really didn't want to be there. She hated the fact that I had to have nurses in the house to help me, although this was not as yet a full-time matter. I could often hear her saying to her friends that she did not know how long she could put up with it and they would respond that she should put me in a home. What annoyed me was I knew I wasn't ready for that yet, but in any event, of course, I had made provisions knowing what the future would bring.

James helped me find the two nurses to start with and they had to put up with Phoebe's arrogance and snobbery. I don't know why but they stayed with me through thick and thin, but thankfully they did. That was until my accident.

I remember one of the nurses was doing something or other when I decided to get up and walk round. I often did this. I suppose it was just something to do. Anyway, I got out of the chair and wandered aimlessly out of my room to the top of the stairs. Whether I simply lost my footing or had forgotten that the steps were there is another matter. However, the result was I fell down the entire staircase, bumping round the curve and finishing on the floor in the middle of the hall.

I remember the terrible pain and that feeling of being unable to move. The nurse came running down the stairs shouting for help but was only able to raise Mrs Cripp.

'Go and get Mrs Stephens and call an ambulance,' she yelled, at which Mrs Cripp speedily left.

I heard Phoebe shout at her, 'What now. Am I never going to be allowed any peace?'

'Shall I call an ambulance?' asked the nurse.

'Is it really necessary?' Phoebe replied as she deigned to come to the scene.

'Yes it is. David had broken his leg badly and he needs urgent attention.'

'It is Mr Stephens to you, young lady, and don't forget it.'

The ambulance arrived and I was whisked off to hospital to accident and emergency department and then put on an orthopedic ward after an operation to reset the bone. It was a very difficult break and I was to be in hospital for at least three weeks.

Phoebe, the cruel bitch, didn't even tell anyone that I had been taken to hospital and had instructed the others not to tell anyone as she said she wanted to do it. If it hadn't been for Mrs Cripp, who secretly phoned Hannah, no one would have ever known. Hannah was my first visitor eight days after I had been admitted; she had been away in Ireland on business and didn't find out about it until her return.

Thinking about this made me agitated and I began calling out which brought the nurses running in.

'What on earth is the matter, David?' they asked. 'You sound as though you are in pain, are you?'

'I was in pain. I was remembering when I broke my leg.'

'David, well done, you are answering me,' the nurse said. 'Have you got any pain now?'

But I couldn't answer again; I had gone back in my shell.

'No? Well lie down and I'll cover you up. Just ring the bell if you need me, or call out, we're only just round the corner.'

I can't sleep, I just can't stop thinking, my whole life seems to be going through my head. God I must be drowning. That's what happens doesn't it? Your whole life passes through your mind. I can't stand this anymore.

I was thinking about Hannah and her coming to see me in hospital and was angry.

'Dad what on earth have you done?' she asked as she leaned over and kissed me.

My brain was at this moment on fullers and not this earth; I could not answer, although I did try to smile.

'Nurse, what are you doing to my father?' Hannah called over to the unfortunate girl who was passing. 'The bed stinks of wee. For god's sake change the sheets.'

'I'll get Sister to speak to you,' she replied.

The sister came eventually and began talking about me as though I was not there and at the same time treating Hannah as though she was an insolent little girl who did not understand. I remember Hannah blasting her and the sister responding: 'He won't eat; we have tried to encourage him to no avail. I think he is just too idle. Yes, he is just too idle to go to the toilet or even ask us to take him and he is constantly messing the bed and I can tell you, young lady, we haven't got time to fuss around him. There are many that are equally as poorly.'

Hannah took the sister round the corner away from me. I suppose in the hope that I would not hear the conversation, but she was so annoyed and loud that I did hear.

'Are you bloody stupid? Can't you see my dad has got dementia? It's a bloody disgrace. Sometimes he forgets how to eat and has to be helped. Sometimes he has to be taken to the toilet or he may wet the bed. Why the hell is he on a ward where no one wants to help him? Have you spoken to his doctor?'

'We don't know who he is,'

'Why not, for god's sake?'

They walked back to me, continuing the conversation. The sister was now visibly shaken, not only from the onslaught, but also from the fact that they had been caught out for not even bothering to check what was wrong with me.

'We have left messages at his home for someone to contact us but no one has. He constantly calls out for Constance. Is that his wife?'

'No, it's my dad's nurse. Hasn't my mother been in to see him?'

'No one has been.'

'I really don't believe this. Please, Sister, sort the matter out quickly. I will telephone my dad's doctor and get something done from that side.'

Hannah stayed with me for a couple of hours and then things began to move, but not for the better. I was transferred to a geriatric ward where everyone seemed worse than me. The other patients couldn't talk to me, the nurses were too busy to stop for a few minutes to chat, so I was just stuck in a chair and left to rot. I remember, however, they did take me to the loo, give me clean sheets and help me eat, and I did come round a little after Hannah had been and began to feed myself

It was here I remember one of the most degrading things that can happen to a man in my predicament; I was bedding down for the night, when a young trainee nurse came to put a bloody nappy on me in the most patronising manner known to man.

'Hello, David, I've come to stop you wetting the bed; tonight we are going to have a big nappy on, aren't we?'

No training given, just a slip of a teenage kid, doing this to me.

I couldn't answer, but I could move and move I did, pushing and snarling as I did so.

'Come on David, don't be silly,' she continued as she pulled back the bedclothes, not even bothering to pull the screens round me before doing so.

I was furious and venting my anger so much that she called for assistance. Thank god for common sense at last.

'Nurse,' the sister shouted. 'Pull the screens round Mr Stephens and do not behave like that.'

I actually said thank you, which amazed all those around.

'Sorry, Mr Stephens,' the young nurse added, following the sister's example of behaviour.

The hospital staff were not geared up for helping dementia patients with broken bones, with the result they were often put on the general ward where they would be out of their depth and very sad and lost.

Often there is an affinity with the patients in the dementia ward; they join forces, pair up, chat to each other, but in the orthopedic wards we are an embarrassment to the others. They do not want to be associated with odd people. I did not realise until I became one how difficult it was and then I was one of the lucky ones, I did have times when I was almost normal, but for some their treatment was uncaring and often cruel.

I remember when Phoebe deigned to visit for the first time and thankfully Hannah was with me. She laced into her mother for being cruel, arrogant, ignorant and a classic snob and all this in front of the entire ward. Those words of encouragement from Hannah stopped any further visits from Phoebe.

Once again I felt the slowing down of my faculties and when Constance found out where I was and came to visit, I greeted her with, 'Oh Constance, I don't like this airport, can we go home?' She just hugged me as though I was her baby and needed security.

I stayed in hospital for three weeks and by the time I was allowed out with an enormous pot on, I was well rested and had not deteriorated further, as everyone had done their best to help me. But as the inevitable day of release into Phoebe's care arrived, I began to suffer from the anxiety, particularly as the ambulance took me home to be greeted by Phoebe, with the welcoming tones, 'Oh it's you is it? Bring him in and take him upstairs.'

That was that. I was immediately shunted out of the way and stayed there until Constance hired a people carrier to take me to her house.

'Can he stay with you for a few days?' Phoebe asked.

'Of course,' Constance replied. 'I would like the help of the nurses, though. He's a bit heavy with that pot on.'

'I'll see to it straight away,' Phoebe said as if anything was preferable to having me around.

'When shall I bring him back?'

'Don't.'

I've never had anyone hate me so much as she obviously did.

She had wanted me out of the way from the word go. There was never any love. Perhaps it showed that I didn't want to get married. Perhaps she resented the pre-nuptial agreement. Perhaps she resented not having any say in the business, but that had been impossible as every time she met the employees she lorded it over them and upset them. I don't know what it was that made her the way she was, but every possible time she could cause me trouble she would, and as my next of kin she had ultimate control of my destiny.

I remember it was this latter situation that Phoebe began to realise was her trump card, especially when she changed GP from James to a Stanley Banham. He had been recommended by one of her ilk for apparently being sympathetic to the partners of those suffering dementia. She knew she wouldn't stand a chance with James as her doctor, as he was my friend and protector.

She really did pull the wool over his eyes, telling him she had no sleep, that I was always getting up in the middle of the night and wandering off and of course that she suffered violence and abuse from me.

Dr Banham was so worried about her he suggested that I be taken into care for a couple of weeks so that she could have a rest, particularly as I still had the enormous plaster cast on my leg. He also suggested that she keep a diary of all the events which, he told her, would prove the situation when things became more difficult later on.

This meant she had to have me back home as she failed to tell the good doctor that I was living in Constance's care and she only had me for a maximum of four days a week, sometimes only two.

I stayed with Phoebe for two weeks and when she had had enough, she called in the doctor, showed him the diary and he was suitably impressed and began to explain the possibilities to her.

'The respite is the best solution at the moment. I will arrange to have him taken to the nursing home for two weeks. Who is his local doctor? I must have a word with him, or her.'

'It's a him and his name is James Percival.'

'Oh, I know James; I'll give him a ring.'

Phoebe was anxious to move things along too hastily for her own good as she persuaded him to ring James there and then.

'James. Stan Banham here. I've got Mrs Stephens with me and she is having difficulty with her husband so I am arranging two weeks respite for him at the Lindisfarne. Have you any problem with that?'

I could hear the conversation as James replied. 'No, not at all. But what about his almost full-time carer, and the nursing cover he has twenty-four hours a day?'

'I'll ring you back.' Banham was a little confused as he asked Phoebe to explain, and of course the lies came out.

'His carer no longer wants to do the job and as for the nurses, they are so unreliable, I can't count on them.'

We had been talking for about half an hour when the doorbell rang and Mrs Cripp popped in to tell us the doctor was at the door.

'Tell him I'm busy,' she snapped.

'It's not you he wants to speak to Mrs Stephens, it's David he wants.'

James followed Mrs Cripp into the lounge and joined us.

'Hello, Stan, how are you?' he said.

'Not bad, thanks. I was just arranging for David to go to Lindisfarne for a couple of weeks,'

'Phoebe, he can go to Constance's for as long as you want and you know it. What's all this about?'

'I'm fed up, worn out and I want him in a home. I can't put up with this much longer.'

'Phoebe, how long have we known each other nearly forty years? Do you honestly believe it's in David's best interests to put him in a home? He has paid for twenty-four hour nursing cover and you pay Constance to have him. Isn't that good enough? And let me tell you it really not in your best interests to do this.'

'How dare you tell me what is in my best interests! I know what is in my best interests and having him here is not.'

'Well, that settles it; he can go to Constance's and stay there until you want him back. Is that satisfactory?'

She had dug a hole for herself and had no alternative but to agree. James made the arrangements straight away and I was shipped back to Constance within the hour. It really was like going back home though.

I had won the battle but not the war.

At last the day came to have the plaster cast removed it was paradise. I came out of the hospital with a clean pair of trousers on, instead of those that had been modified for the purpose, and to actually try and walk on my own, despite all its difficulties, was a joy. I felt freer and my brain seemed to click into action, and for a short while I began to feel near normal, especially after I was taken to lunch by Hannah and Constance.

Things were pretty good for a few years I seemed to be in remission as the pace of deterioration had definitely slowed; that was until my granddaughter Elizabeth's fourth birthday and as usual Phoebe had promised to take her shopping. I remember that day very well as Hannah telephoned me with an invitation to join them on the shopping trip to Beatties, together with the two children and what grandfather would miss an opportunity like that.

Beatties was a large departmental store in Warstones, but most importantly it had a huge toy shop in it. It was every child's dream and I even remember being taken there by my father when I was young. Phoebe parked the car, helped me out and spent the next ten minutes as we walked with the family into the store asking if I was all right, with me becoming somewhat impatient and assuring her I was.

I remember as we entered the shop we walked into the women's wear section. It was a huge floor and there were hundreds of dresses on display and of course this was too much for Phoebe; she just had to look at all the new stock, before we made our way to the basement and the toys. Phoebe was on her own, whilst Hannah and the children were together and somehow I got detached from them. I started to panic, I couldn't see anyone that I knew and yelled 'Constance' at the top of my voice. I sat down on a nearby stool crying. Hannah had heard my scream and came hurrying to me. I was still in tears when she arrived but this time I was surrounded by people who naturally were concerned for me, which made me feel even worse as I didn't know them.

'Are you all right dad?' Hannah asked as she gestured to the well-wishers, thanking them for their concern.

'What's the matter with Granddad?' Elizabeth asked her mother.

'Oh, he's not very well and got lost. He's just a little confused at the moment. He'll be all right.'

This little girl came up to me, held out her hand and simply said, 'Come on, Granddad. Hold my hand. I'll look after you.'

She took my hand and held on to me as though I was in her care, turning round several times, looking up to my eyes as she guided me away from the rows of clothes rails.

I remember I couldn't do any other than follow her out and strangely I felt confident when she held my hand.

I must have been sobbing my heart out as I thought of that moment as it drew the attention of the night sister.

'David, what on earth is upsetting you, you're crying?'

I actually responded, 'I was thinking about my lovely little grand-daughter and how she helped me.'

'Would you like a cup of tea?'

'No thanks,'

'Well, David, you must try and get some sleep.'

She left me and went back to the nurses' station, but I couldn't sleep, I just kept going back to my thoughts and couldn't let go of them.

Now where was I? Oh yes I remember I was in Beatties.

I could see the other people looking at me and for the first time I recognised the signs that they didn't want to be near me. It may be catching. I noticed Phoebe almost hiding away, trying to avoid being seen with me and only surfacing when she thought everything was back to normal and no one would be able to associate her with the problem.

'Hello, you lot. Where have you been hiding, I've been looking everywhere for you?' she said addressing the grandchildren; but Hannah had seen everything and rounded on her.

'You nasty individual, Mum, how could you do that to Dad?'

'Don't be silly dear,' she replied in a most condescending manner and then added,' Come on children, let's go to see the toys.'

The Dragon simply shrugged it off and marched off with our grandchildren, holding Max's hand very firmly as if to make a point that he was with her.

Elizabeth continued to hold my hand, still looking round, until I said, 'Go on, darling, I'm all right now. Thank you.' With that she skipped off to join her brother whilst Hannah walked with me.

'Are you sure you are all right, Dad?'

'Yes, I'm fine now, Hannah. Don't worry.'

We had a wonderful couple of hours wandering round the toy department and the rest of the store, followed by lunch, with no further hitches on my side. In fact for the next two to three weeks I had no problems at all. I was taking the medication and even when I went home for the odd day, Constance telephoned to make sure I had had the tablets.

It had become obvious to everybody that I was not only fond

of Constance but I was also dependent on her and for the first time I heard the wagging tongues. Phoebe's friends were implying that there was more than a nurse-patient relationship between us and that she should watch out. I could see a real change in Phoebe and not for the first time I began to get the impression that Phoebe was becoming jealous of Constance, so much so she felt I ought to go back home.

I hated the political football role I was playing as every time it unsettled me and I lost another percentage point off my brain capacity, none the less I had to return home and what was worse I had only been home for less than twenty-four hours when Phoebe shouted at me for getting under her feet. I was never to go into the kitchen again, she told me, and I was to stay away from this and that; in fact, as long as I was in my room everything was all right.

This row unsettled me and I once again slipped out of normal mode and decided I would go to work again.

I asked for the car keys but was not given them and then I threatened Phoebe that if she did not take me I would go on my own, so I did.

I really don't know how I got there but eventually I did and was met by Alf the gatekeeper. He telephoned home but the Dragon wouldn't talk to him; she then sent a nurse to pick me up and from that moment on it became part of their job to pick me up from wherever I wandered to. They loved it as they always drove my Rolls-Royce. I did make myself a nuisance when I wanted a lift to see my mother and father or go back to the office, but eventually everyone became accustomed to my extraordinary behaviour.

I was often at home for a couple of weeks before the dragon had a dinner party or simply got fed up with me and then I'd be sent back to Constance for a few weeks before I would reluctantly go back. During the time with Constance she always kept up her efforts to keep my brain going with all the brain exercises and the constant conversations. She also encouraged me to read the paper and would test me on what I had read or we would discuss a topic, to see if I had understood it.

Every four weeks she would take me to see James for a check-up and then to the specialist to see what my current status was. Unfortunately, every month there had been a very slight deterioration. They analysed what I had done during that period, how things had been at home and it was becoming clear that the more stress I had the quicker the process worsened, but also it happened when I had periods of inactivity, which I had when I was with Phoebe and banished to my room. The golden rules were set in stone; keep active and avoid stress – but it wasn't always possible.

There was one occasion during this period I remember well: Phoebe had been given a bit of stick from a friend during one of my stays with her. It started quite simply with a simple, 'Hello, David, not with Constance today then?'

I didn't ignore her intentionally, I was just a bit slow, and in fact I stuttered a little which stupidly the woman countered.

'I hit a spot did I, David?'

'What do you mean?' Phoebe stammered 'David go in the study, I want to talk to Lesley for a minute.'

I dutifully got up and sauntered out of the room and made my way to the study, leaving the door open.

'What did you mean by that, Lesley?'

'Darling, it's nothing; it's just what people are saying, that you are throwing him at Constance Redpath. Everyone can see she loves him and you are laying it on a plate.'

'For god's sake, Lesley, he's no use to anyone, you know what he's like I pay her to look after him.'

'I know that, and you do, but it's what people are saying. That they sleep together and that it's not a proper nurse-patient relationship. They have even been seen in Windermere walking arm in arm, bold as brass.'

'How do you know that?' Phoebe asked, becoming more and more shocked with each revelation.

'Oh, it's just what people are saying, you know what they are like. I just wanted to let you know, so at least you could do something.'

It was seldom that Phoebe was at a loss for words, but when I returned from the study to see if I could go back in the lounge, like a good little boy, I could tell that Lesley Cole had enjoyed every moment of Phoebe's discomfort, despite their supposed close friendship.

Phoebe was too upset to send me away again, instead she tolerated my presence and the three of us sat and drank tea and the subject was dropped.

It wasn't often I was clever enough to pretend I was having a turn, but this time I managed it. I thought I could at least protect Constance by distracting the two women from talking about us further. I was sitting in my chair when I decided I wanted to go to the toilet.

'I want to go to the toilet.' I said quietly.

'Well go on then,' Phoebe responded sharply.

I sat still for a minute or two with both women looking at me in total surprise, unable to say anything and then suddenly I announced, 'Too late I've done it.'

'What!' Phoebe exclaimed. 'Nurse Wilson,' she yelled at the top of her voice. 'Get out of here, you dirty devil, and go and clean yourself up.' She turned to Lesley and said, 'And you say they are having an affair. Well, they are welcome to it. Would you put up with that, from Jack?'

'No I wouldn't, he would have been put in a home long ago.'

'That's my problem: Constance Redpath is the nursing home.'

I remember going up to my room desperately trying not to laugh, falling onto my bed and pushing the pillow over my face to deaden the sound as I laughed and laughed and laughed.

'You are a terrible person, David.' The dulcet tones of Nurse Wilson disturbed my moment. She had twigged what I had done was only to shock them. I put my finger to her lips and said, 'Sssshhhh,' and we were both trying to stop laughing by now.

148

I didn't hear anything else except a shouted 'Goodbye, David' as the lovely trouble-stirring Lesley left us to sort out the mess she had started.

It didn't take long for Phoebe to order Constance's presence at the palace. Constance arrived full of trepidation and what was worse Phoebe answered the door to her, which prevented me giving her a warning.

'Ah, Constance my dear, come on in. Go straight into the lounge and I'll get Mrs Cripp to bring us tea.'

I didn't even get chance to say anything then as she was back in the lounge before I could blink an eye.

'Constance I'll get straight to the point,' Phoebe began. 'I have just been told you are sleeping with my husband and that the two of you are having an affair. You have been seen in Windermere together and I gather that you have stayed in a hotel together.'

Constance burst out laughing.

'It's not funny, Constance. What have you got to say for yourself?'

'Don't be so silly, Phoebe. You have been reading too many Mills and Boon books, or listening to too much gossip from your so-called friends.'

'Now look here—'

Constance interrupted, 'No, you look here. David is ill and he has lost all his confidence. He needs someone to care for him. You haven't got the time, Phoebe, or the inclination. Do you look after him when he can't feed himself properly or go to the toilet? Do you dress him when he gets confused? Do you go out looking for him when he gets lost in the garden? Do you look after him when he can't dress himself properly? No you bloody don't. AND,' she said, raising her voice, 'if you think I am going to worry about some mindless idiots' gossip, none of whom would give a blind man a light, then Phoebe darling you are mistaken. If you want the responsibility you must take it but you cannot stop me from helping him. And yes, I am fond of him. Who wouldn't be? He's a lovely man but it is apparent that you don't think so.'

I had been standing at the open door of the lounge listening to this and even in my confused state it felt wonderful that someone had stood up for me. Phoebe was at a loss for words and was obviously thankful when Mrs Cripp came in with the tea as it at least enabled her to recover and put some thoughts together.

The first one that came into her head was to ask whether I had changed my pants.

'He's just wet himself, you know. It was so embarrassing. I had Lesley Cole with me and we did not know where to put ourselves.'

Constance looked at me and struggled to stop herself laughing as she caught my sly wink.

'Is he like this often?' Phoebe asked, trying to make conversation.

'Of course he is,' Constance told her. 'But it's something you have to put up with, particularly in town, or in cold weather. It's when he forgets how to eat that it's most difficult and I have to teach him, or feed him in the restaurant. Phoebe, you mustn't worry what the likes of Lesley Cole say; we all know she and one or two others from the group have slept around themselves.'

'Yes, I suppose you're right,' Phoebe said, now somewhat deflated.

'Do you want me to continue to look after David?'

'Yes, of course.'

'Then I will. Come on, David, I'll take you back to my place. Nurse Wilson can go early. Phoebe, just give me a ring if there are any problems or if you feel David should come home, we are only fifteen minutes away.'

Phoebe settled for that and I had a more relaxed time away from her, which did improve my lot. However, I started getting wanderlust again whether I was at home or with Constance and I often found myself at the factory or back with Philip Russell. At least they now knew me and would telephone Constance to pick me up or even arrange for a taxi to take me straight home. It was about this time when Constance thought a long walk each day would perhaps make me tired and then I would be less likely to wander off.

I remember one lovely sunny Sunday afternoon and we were walking through the village and saw some of ladies and gentleman playing bowls. It fascinated me so much so I thought I would like to watch. We stopped and stood looking through the railings and on to the green for a few minutes before being invited into the ground to sit and watch. I was almost like a kid with a new toy watching this sport for the first time.

We sat on the benches and eventually several people began to talk to us. It was difficult for them as when I was dressed up and walking along or standing with Constance, I didn't look like an imbecile – as Phoebe would call me. In fact, I could look quite distinguished and businesslike. However, when they came up to talk to me and found I was only fifty per cent in working order they were somewhat embarrassed and left quickly to talk about me behind my back. I remember one or two had worked for Pennington's and they at least knew my problem and would understand. Constance, however, would always introduce me to everyone to make sure I was involved.

We made several visits to the club just to watch and the members began to talk to me with less and less difficulty, so much so I put it on my list of places to wander to.

Of course on the first and second occasion no one knew where the hell I was, until they found me wandering trying to find my way home; following which I would suddenly find myself turning up to watch matches on a Wednesday and Friday, which caused great consternation to both Phoebe and Constance, as they didn't know where I was, and of course to the teams who were playing. On the fourth or fifth occasion the club began to telephone Constance and tell her I was there and an hour later she would pick me up.

Gradually they got to know me and someone invited me into the clubhouse for a drink and from then on I seemed to go in every time I visited. No, I remember now, it wasn't quite like that, I was sitting watching a match on one of the benches when play was halted by a shower of rain. I remained sitting on the bench getting soaking wet when a member took pity on me and invited me in.

'Come on, David, you can't sit there getting wet. Come inside.' He took my arm and gently encouraged me in.

That was the start, Constance paid my subscription and I was then allowed into the bar to have a drink whenever I wanted to and they put up with me, warts an all.

I didn't want to be the silly old bugger in the corner but inevitably, that's what I was. Sometimes I could converse quite intelligently and talk on a variety of subjects but at other times I would talk gibberish and jabber away, with no one listening.

I felt comfortable there though, and although some people found it awkward to be in my company, the majority allowed me to sit with them. I don't know whether it was because they were pensioners themselves or that they too felt old, but whatever it was they didn't feel sorry for me and seemed to understand. Some perhaps feared, there but for the grace of god go I.

They often tried to include me in the conversation, but in the main I just sat in their group, having a drink and lost in thought. Many times when there was a match on I was happy to sit by myself in the clubhouse and just while away the time. Constance thought it was good for me and would often put twenty pound behind the bar for me to pay for a round of drinks. It was a useful arrangement as it meant I never had to sponge on anyone.

I remember one Sunday the club had a gala or fair during which time several important matches were played. It was the height of the season. I was alone in the bar sitting in a corner drinking my Ansell's Mild Beer when two young men came into the bar and began chatting to the steward. They turned and looked at me, 'Who's that bloke' one of them asked.

'That's David. Poor chap has got Alzheimer's and he's not in this world. He doesn't know what's going on. He just sits there staring into space. I suppose he's harmless enough.'

It was awful to hear yourself being described like that, but I suppose that's how I appeared to the outside of my world.

A few more people came in and chatted to me but I was in one of those moods when I couldn't return the conversation, even in gibberish, so they soon left me to myself. The young men bought drinks and sat nearby 'taking the piss out of me' but I didn't bite, I just stared at them with a vacant look and then it was, 'What are you staring at old man?'

Their banter continued for a few minutes, before they were politely told to stop, which they did. They hung around drinking for a while and then left, but shortly afterwards returned. The place was empty, mainly because it was such a sunny day and drinks were being served outside.

Suddenly they pounced. One grabbed the steward by his lapels and pulled him over the counter and the other ran behind the back of the bar. They grabbed the money from the till and ran. The whole incident only took a few seconds and I hadn't the wit to do anything, except when they had gone I struggled outside and made a piercing yell and all came running in. I pointed to the bar and someone ran behind. The steward had been stabbed and was bleeding badly. They phoned for the police and an ambulance and the man was taken to hospital. Thankfully, after a few weeks he recovered and came back to work.

The police asked lots of questions when they arrived, but of course I was no real help and allowed to go back home, to Constance's that is. They had no clues, there was no CCTV, and anyway who would have thought that a bowls club full of the retired gentry would be worth robbing. The youths had taken over three hundred pounds from the till though, which was a huge some for the club. It turned out they had had a special licence for the gala day and it was that which attracted the undesirables.

I was suffering from shock when Constance came to pick me up and I couldn't even tell her what had gone on and the cause of all the police activity. We had a cup of tea when we got back to her home and tried to relax but I couldn't so she thought it better if I went to bed.

The following day things were no better when the police arrive to obtain a statement from me as the only witness to the crime, other than the steward, who was in hospital. Even after he was discharged he could not remember much as it had all happened too quickly.

The inspector along with a WPC knocked on the door.

'Good morning, I'm Inspector Willis of West Yorkshire Police and this is Constable Grice,' It was a name which came to haunt me later on. 'Is David Stephens in?'

'Yes he is,' Constance replied.

'Is it about the incident at the bowls club?' she asked.

'Yes, may we come in?'

'Of course but I don't think you will get anywhere with David. He's in shock at the moment and may not be able to help. He has dementia.'

'Can we see him?'

'Of course,' Constance replied, leading them into the dining room where I was just finishing my breakfast.

Constance stayed near me all the time, putting her hand on my shoulder to give me confidence.

'Good morning, Mr Stephens,' the inspector began and then introduced his colleague. I nodded and this unfortunately gave them the false impression that I understood everything that was going on.

'I would like to talk to you about the robbery at the bowls club; I understand you were sitting in the bar at the time?'

I nodded

'Did you see everything from start to finish?'

'Yes.'

'Could you describe the people?'

'Yes,' I replied as the young WPC took out her notebook.

I didn't say another word which made the inspector lose his patience a little. 'Well go on then.'

'You'll have to be patient, Inspector,' Constance said. 'David has great difficulty expressing himself sometimes.'

Then I began. 'The one lad had very thick jet black hair and a round face and thick black eyebrows.'

The WPC was making copious notes as the inspector went on with his questions. 'What was this one wearing?'

'He had a red and black striped sweater and black trousers, grey socks and black shoes.'

'What was the sweater like? Was it thin stripes or thick stripes? Did they go top to bottom or round?'

'They were thick stripes going round.'

'Was there anything else that could identify the men?'

'Yes.' I stopped speaking again to the growing impatience of the inspector as the whole interview was being conducted at a snail's pace.

'What was that then?' he asked.

'He had a big sack on his back.'

'What colour was the sack?'

'Black'

'Were there any other identifying marks on the sack?'

'Yes.'

'Can you remember what they were?'

'Yes'

'What were they, Mr Stephens?'

'Big white letters,'

'Can you remember what they said?'

'Yes'

'What were they, Mr Stephens?' the inspector continued this time with a purposeful deep sigh as the WPC sat poised ready with the notebook.

'S.W.A.G.'

She wrote it down and after a minute or so the penny dropped with her and she showed the inspector. I had described accurately Dennis the Menace from the Beano or Dandy, a comic I used to read when I was a child.

The two officers looked at each other in exasperation and then to Constance who was desperately trying not to laugh. I remember I was oblivious to what I had done and I suppose I was waiting for a, well done David, which Constance duly gave and then directed the officer to the front door.

'I did warn you,' she remarked. 'He's not always as bad as this but I think he is still in shock. I'll let you know when he is ready to answer your questions.'

'No, don't worry, Mrs Stephens.'

'Redpath.'

They looked quizzically at her.

'My name is Constance Redpath. I'm David's carer; he lives with me several days a week.'

'Well Mrs Redpath, I don't think we'll bother you again.'

She closed the door behind them, burst out laughing and put her arms round me. 'David you're wonderful,' she said.

I continued to wander down to the club many times, just for the company and to give everyone a bit of peace. I can't remember if anything was ever said to me about the incident.

A few weeks later Constance took me on our usual trip to Harrogate, we had a wander round the shops as we always did, and then went to lunch. It was after lunch when we were walking towards WH Smiths that I noticed on the other side of the road, Dennis the Menace, the lad who had stabbed the steward at the club – and I recognised him. I wasn't behaving too badly at the time and remarked to Constance that I knew who he was.

'Are you sure dear?' she asked, sounding as though she didn't want to get involved.

'I'm positive.'

'Right then. Let's see where he goes and if we find a policeman we will tell him about it.'

We stood casually looking in the shop window, keeping our eyes on 'Dennis the Menace' through the reflection in the glass, waiting to see what happened. Constance was gripping me like some excited child and I could tell she was enjoying every minute.

'Come on, let's follow him,' she said as he was met by two others and they began to walk towards the Stray. It's amazing how stupid you can be sometimes, neither of us had thought of using the mobile phones to contact the police until we saw someone else using a phone.

'We are walking on the Leeds Road towards the Stray following a group of three youths, one of which my husband had positively identified as the man who stabbed the steward at the bowls club a few weeks ago.'

I loved it, she had said my husband and it made me feel so . . . ooooh so good that I shivered with enjoyment.

Constance had to repeat the story to the duty officer, but at least he had his wits about him.

'Keep your phone open so we can keep in contact. Tell me where you are and we will be out immediately.'

We followed at a discreet distance, describing what they were wearing and of course the direction they were travelling in. It was not long before we heard the sound of sirens, which then suddenly stopped. We found out later that they did not want to spook the three lads.

Constance gave directions and the lads' position and then the police cars arrived, one to the rear, one to the front and an unmarked car to the right of them. Within seconds all three lads were in custody. We walked up to the where the officers held them and I identified the one young man who I had seen that day.

'I was nowhere near the place and anyway, you're supposed to be brainless so how would you know?'

I had to smile at the stupidity of the young man. How on earth would he know I had dementia unless he had been there. It was almost a confession. He did eventually confess to the crime but the other man was not caught. I did not have to give evidence since he pleaded guilty, but as the prosecutor said, had he not made the mistake of showing he recognised me, he would have got away with it because there would be doubt about my condition.

I was a hero for the day and did have the offer of many drinks at the club. It was all too soon yesterday's news, but it was nice for the moment.

Chapter 12

I suppose the constant wandering off to see Constance or to go to my other venues, plus of course my mood swings and strange behaviour, must have been a bit wearing for Phoebe, particularly as she hadn't the patience to deal with it. But instead of trying to improve matters sympathetically and using the services I had organised in advance, she was still determined to make a show of it all being too much for her. Her motive was simply one of greed. She used the hard-luck story, how she was struggling to keep everything together, how difficult it was for her to help me when I was having a bad day. She told people that I kept her up all night worrying and that she hadn't had a proper night's sleep for weeks. Now what became apparent was she had been drip-feeding my boys, and in particular their wives, with all this rubbish and was enlisting their help to get rid of me.

Hannah told me she was using the philanthropic technique; actually having pleasant little conversations with each of their wives in turn.

'Wendy' – who was Josh's wife – 'you know we really do have a lot of money and I hate to see you struggle. I think you should have some of your inheritance now. I'm sure it would help you'

What person would not be tempted by that? This was then followed by the *coup de grâce*? 'We've got over one and a half million in cash and I think you should have at least quarter each.'

Over three hundred and fifty thousand each was on offer just to get me out of the way. She then made the same offer to the others and of course the wives began to work on each other and their husbands, who didn't need a lot of pushing, as they were already mummy's favourites. They only had one problem, Hannah, and she was an even bigger one than me.

Wendy, Josh's wife was somewhat akin to Phoebe and I'm sure that's why she chose her for him. I remember she influenced all three boys in their choice of wives. She always welcomed the girls she approved of with open arms, bought them expensive presents on their birthdays and at Christmas. She told the lads how much they were suited and invited the girls to family functions, simply pushing them together.

It worked, as she was able to manipulate them from the word go, and the mere fact she had always ruined the boys by letting them have what they wanted, they were putty in her hands. She had long divided them from me.

Hannah, as I've said before, was a different kettle of fish. She was always an independent thinker and after university even more so. She had developed a spirit of fighting for the little man; supporting those in need and above all believed in fairness wherever it was needed.

She had gained a great deal of respect from the workforce at Pennington's where she had improved the welfare system, revised the pension arrangements and increased the holiday entitlement, with all the costs being borne by the company. She had taken a leaf from her grandfather's book and knew the names of all the eighty odd employees.

This is what the opposition was up against but with seven of them against her, the odds weren't even. She would come and talk to me about the meetings they had; how Wendy would try and use the same technique as Phoebe on her, telling her the money would set her up for life and she wouldn't have to slave away for Pennington's anymore. It was all a waste of effort anyway, she went on, as Phoebe was going to sell it when I was dead or when she had a power of attorney.

It was around this time I confessed to Hannah that I had given my shares in the business to Constance and that she had left them to her in her will, although Constance actually wanted to give her the business as soon as she had become established in the firm. This revelation gave her much enjoyment as she was busily negotiating her way through the family mire.

Their first family meeting was a cracker, as Wendy had invited all the family and their spouses to dinner one evening with the express purpose of sorting out ways to get their hands on the money.

They sat round in the lounge with a drink each, simply looking at one another and talking trivia. No one wanted to begin the conversation, or be the first to condemn me.

Hannah decided she would be devil's advocate and said, 'Wendy what's all this about then. You've never invited us to dinner before, so why now? You must have some ulterior motive.'

Wendy coughed and spluttered and was rescued from her embarrassment by Josh who angrily said, 'You know bloody well what it's all about. Don't play the innocent with me.'

'No, I don't. Something about my father's money I believe.'

'Look Hannah, you know bloody well what it's about. Mother has offered to give each of us three hundred thousand pounds and I for one would find that very useful. Wouldn't the rest of you?'

The other two sheep bleated their acknowledgement that they were in agreement.

'Come on, Josh, where do you think she's going to get that sort of money from. She's that stupid, every penny she's had she's spent. Anyway, what are we plotting to do? Support dear momma in her quest to get her hands on Dad's money? Don't you think she's harmed him enough?'

Wendy tried to interrupt and put her two penneth in but was stamped on hard by Hannah, who said, 'Since when have you any say in what the family does with its money. Leave it to the grown-ups. Though, mind you, I can't see many round here.'

161

I could imagine what the atmosphere was like at that moment.

'Don't talk to Wendy like that. You can now see the reason why you haven't been invited before,' said Josh.

Both Simon and William tried to calm the situation down. 'Come on, you two, this arguing won't get us anywhere.'

'Seriously, Hannah, wouldn't you like to have the three hundred K?'

'Not particularly, we don't need it do we, Donald? I get a good salary from Pennington's and that does us.'

'But for how long?' Josh asked, as though he was party to some secret.

'As long as I keep working I suppose.'

'Do you think you'll be kept on when mother sells it?'

Hannah burst out laughing and told them she couldn't.

'Oh yes she can. Dad's lost his marbles and mother is going to get a power of attorney and when she does she will give us the money there and then.'

'She can't, she gets an allowance from Pennington's which is very generous but that could stop at any time. Can you see a firm buying the company and continuing to give her an allowance, which incidentally Dad still pays the tax on. I'll tell you this, you will have no chance of either you or mother ever of getting your hands on Pennington's and if mother doesn't stop this dreadful business, *I'll* do my best to stop her allowance. Dad couldn't trust her with the bank accounts and you can see why. She doesn't own the company so how on earth would Mother, the greedy bitch, get her hands on it?'

'You know very well she will get control in the end anyway, it is only a matter of time before Dad is found to be incapable of managing his affairs, and she *will* have a power of attorney and be able to sign the cheques and draw out of the accounts and control Pennington's. Then we can have our money,' Josh added triumphantly.

'My, you have it all worked out. You're going to shove Dad in a home, get him certified and take his money.'

'Look Hannah,' Josh chipped in, 'you know as well as I do it's only a matter of time, so as Mother said, we might as well have it now when it can do us the most good.'

'It's the family's money not just his,' William said.

'Oh, you let him speak do you?' Hannah said, addressing Toni.

'Well, it's not the family's money, its Dad's money, to look after him. And anyway, who made it? Who worked every day to keep us in the lifestyle others would envy.'

'Oh, Hannah, get off your bloody socialist soap box. We're talking about us.'

'Josh, you're just like mother, selfish and cruel and up your own arse and it will be over my dead body that you succeed in taking it.'

'Hannah,' Josh said, 'we've already spoken to our lawyers and they have told mother that she can do it and she will, with or without you.'

'We have been busy, haven't we? I don't think I want to have dinner with you lot. You're bloody wicked and you will find out there are more obstacles to overcome before you have your dream, Josh, you always were a spoiled prat and you two are well suited. You might just as well have married your mother.'

He stormed over to her, shouting, 'What do you mean by that?' His face was almost touching hers as he bent over her snarling.

Donald jumped from where he was sitting and pushed Josh to the floor shouting, 'If you ever do that to Hannah again, you'll not get up. Do you understand?'

'What's the little housewife going to do to me then?' Josh added as Donald moved away, but he didn't leave it that. He grabbed Donald's shoulder, turning him round to face him and then with his supercilious attitude to the fore said, 'Don't you turn your back on me when I'm talking to you.'

Donald didn't wait, he simply threw one good strong punch to the chin and that was the end of that. All that was left was for Wendy to scream, 'Get out! Get out!'

Simon really tried to calm things down to no avail and even Pricilla began screaming 'stop it' in a hysterical high-pitched voice, but all to no avail. As Hannah and Donald were leaving, Josh shouted, 'We'll do it with you or without you and if you don't support Mother you will get nothing.'

'Dream on, Josh. You be careful.'

It was the first time Donald had stood up for Hannah and I must admit it did help to change my opinion of him. I remember Hannah telling me all about their little scheme and although I laughed about it, deep down I was hurt and resentful that my own children could actually sit down to discuss the possibility of getting me certified, just to get their hands on my money.

I know I had never been close to the boys and realise that was my fault and I should have made more effort with them; I should have become more involved with them.

I now realised it was too late to do anything else about my will and arrangements and now they could easily challenge it as I was very often of unsound mind. There was only one thing I could do and that was to discuss it all with Constance, but to my surprise Hannah had already told her about the meeting.

Constance had become extremely worried that Phoebe and the boys would do something soon to get me out of the way and suggested that we see James Percival and our solicitor to talk over the problem with them. James as you can imagine was furious and although I was not fully understanding, he did explain that they would not be allowed 'to put me away' as he called it, without him knowing. He promised it would not happen, as he was my local doctor and of course he was party to the arrangements that had been made.

James also came with us to see Terence our solicitor and he assured us that he had looked into the matter and that there was nothing they could do about all the previous arrangements we'd made. However, there was only really one way they could try and change matters and that could happen if I was sectioned because I had become a danger to myself and others.

'It would still be difficult but not impossible. Won't the children help?' Terence asked.

'Hannah does,' Constance said, 'but the others have been offered a lot of money to support their mother in her efforts to get rid of David. Josh and his wife they have well and truly got the others on their side. I can't believe they would do such a thing, but they are.'

The mere mention of Josh set me off. 'Josh not . . .' I couldn't say anymore; I had lost it. Constance took hold of my hand to give me reassurance, but I could tell she was worried about my reaction to the word Josh.

'Do they know what the terms of the will are and what arrangements David has made for his care?' Terence asked.

They all looked at me, but I couldn't remember anything. In fact, I couldn't take anymore and became very distressed so Constance had to take me home.

James, now acting as my friend, had a private conversation off the record with Terence to find out what Phoebe could do and was assured that if she was not aware of the provisions in the will, or my arrangements, should she put me in a home before I was sectioned, the conditions of my arrangements would come into force. Furthermore, they should not section me without James having some input and with that he could then report what was already available.

Later on that afternoon James came to visit me and explained things simply to reassure me, but I always had the niggling doubt that Phoebe would engage the best lawyers, psychologists and doctors to find a way through.

'David, why did you get cross when Josh was mentioned? Has he done anything or said anything to you?'

I didn't answer.

'Come on love,' Constance encouraged me, 'what's he done?'

It was several days before my brain was able to tell Constance what Phoebe had said and when I did she was as shocked as I was that Phoebe had tricked me into marriage and she could now see why Josh was the favourite and why she had no love for me.

I must admit I felt sorry for Josh for the way in which he had found out that I was not his father. It made no odds for me, as he never showed any real feeling towards me, or at least that's how I felt; but I could now understand the bitterness he was showing in trying to cause the family to gang up on me.

I remember when we had one of our regular meetings with James, Constance told him about Josh, and I was astonished when James told me he already realised that was the case.

'I wasn't sure when you got married, it was only when the baby was born that I began to have my doubts that you were the father. It was confirmed when he had that nasty cut on his leg and was taken to hospital. You remember, David. He fell off his bike.'

I didn't remember so just listened, trying to take it all in.

'It was the blood test he was given at the hospital that alerted me. I had to check it myself to make sure. I couldn't tell you, David; I wasn't allowed to and anyway I didn't want to cause a problem for you or Josh.'

It was water under the bridge and both Constance and I thought it was better to leave things as they were unless Josh wanted to discuss the matter.

This wasn't the worst news I received that day I remember, James told us he wanted to retire. He had had enough of the way he was treated by the National Health Service and what they expected him to do and he was tired of it. He had sold his practice to a Gerald Thumpington and even I couldn't forget that name. What he was did was transfer all the patients to the new regime but dealt with a few on a private basis and thankfully I was one of them. I like to believe he stayed in Practice because of his friendship for me and in one of my more lucid moments I did tell him that business was business and friendship was different. He knew what I meant because even with my condition I knew the insurance was astronomical for him to operate in this way. I was relieved that he was staying and who cared how much it cost I still wanted James nearby. I think it would have finished me there and then had he retired completely; but as he said I would be covered even better than before as I now had two doctors to look after me.

Now where was I? Oh God I've forgotten what I was thinking about, come on think Man. Doctor . . . Constance . . . accident. Oh I remember Josh and Phoebe and him not being my child. It sounds bloody awful to think like that.

I do recall in the distant past, unless it was my imagination playing tricks on me, an argument between Josh and his mother as to why she had not told him before and also why she had to tell him in the way she did, but I don't think he ever asked who his real father was.

I did get my own back on a number of occasions, particularly when I was with Phoebe and had Constance with me and could remember; I would call out the name Josh, or make some cryptic comment about my son Josh. She knew I was deliberately trying to provoke her and she knew that Constance was involved, which I could sense really aggravated her.

Belatedly both Toni and Pricilla provided me with more grandchildren, Toni had a little boy Anthony and Pricilla a daughter, but what was so sad was there were many times when I couldn't recognise them and then there were days when they were frightened of me. They couldn't understand why I was so different. I know the boys would not have discouraged them from seeing me, but I do know that I was an embarrassment; with the result I kept away from them, leaving Phoebe to be the grand dame. It saddened me greatly not to be able to have a relationship with them as I had with Hannah's children, Elizabeth and Max, but I suppose I was very lucky to have had that.

'The plotters', as I remember we called them, decided to have another go at Hannah, my eyes and ears, and once again to meet at Josh's, only this time Phoebe was there and there was no dinner just a cup of coffee and a family row. There was now a sense of urgency to the whole affair, as the children were hungry for the money. Phoebe therefore decided she would be the leading protagonist by telling them all what the situation was.

'Your father is no longer capable of looking after himself,' she began. 'He messes the bed, he wanders off, he doesn't recognise people and he is a nuisance around the house. I have been told that we could put him in a home, where he would be better off; where he would be looked after by proper qualified staff. It won't be long before I am granted power of attorney and then I will be able to decide to do what is best for him.'

'No mother, it's what's best for you perhaps, but not for Dad,' Hannah commented.

'Well, is that so wrong? I've had to put up with such a lot over the last few years. I deserve a better life. Anyway, I realise that I have lost your father in any event, so what is the point of him staying around. I need your support to get the power of attorney straight away, otherwise we will have to wait months, if not years, and I know the money will be useful to you now.'

They were all against Hannah and Donald and for the second time they left in disgust before the end of the discussions.

'Hannah, I promise you this,' Phoebe said. 'When I have control of the finances you will regret this.'

'Not half as much as you will, Mother,' Hannah retorted

They didn't speak to Hannah for several weeks and it strained the family relationships so much that I didn't see my children or other grandchildren very often afterwards.

They, the plotters, working in unison, decided to get me examined by a psychiatrist and another doctor, but thanks to the glorious Mrs Cripp, who told Hannah, who in turn arranged for James to call on the day of the examination, I was protected.

'What do you want?' Phoebe snapped as she saw James at the door.

'I've come to see David. He is my patient, Phoebe.'

'Well you'll just have to come back some other time. He's busy.'

'No, I'm sorry, I'm coming in now,' And with that he marched up to my room. 'Hello, David. How are you today – and who have we here?' he added, looking at two men in the room.

'My name is Smiles,' one of the men replied, 'and more to the point, who are you?'

'I am David's doctor and I would ask you to leave as I need to see him now.'

'But I am examining him,' Smiles protested.

'I said out, now, AND if you want to see my patient, you must first speak to me and ask my permission. Do you understand? Would you agree, David?'

I nodded because at the time that was all I could do.

'What you are doing is totally unprofessional and whilst we are on that subject, I would like to know your names and what you are doing here.'

'You know my name,' said Smiles, 'and this is Doctor Frederick. We have come at the behest of Mrs Stephens to assess the wellbeing of her husband as we are told he is no longer able to make any decisions for himself. Mrs Stephens needs a power of attorney so that she can carry on living normally. She has been unable to draw money from the accounts and she is unable to pay the wages at Pennington's and there is trouble brewing there.'

'Look, before you go any further I will tell you that she has been trying to get hold of David's money for years. David has made provision himself to pay for nursing, even full-time when it arises. His wife has an allowance of approximately £1,500 a week to run the house, excluding bills, for life. The bills are paid by another source. However, despite this large allowance, she is not satisfied. She does not own or have anything to do with Pennington's. Do you agree, David?' Again I nodded.

'Greed causes a great deal of trouble,' James continued, 'and I am afraid that Mrs Stephens is greedy. I think she is at the stage when she will try anything to get her hands on David's money. Do I make myself clear?'

'Crystal.'

'Now, David's condition is a cause for great anxiety, but as long as he takes his medication and is looked after properly by his carer we can avoid all the problems.'

It was round one to me and it proved that if there was just one dissenting voice like Hannah's, it would be impossible for the family to get a power of attorney. And I had made careful arrangements so that there was no need for financial decisions to be made under any circumstances.

They left me alone for a few weeks, except that Phoebe had been advised to keep a diary of all matters concerning me, what I did, how I behaved, where I had wandered off to, and more importantly, how I was reacting to various matters. Of course she did it fastidiously and it was only when dear old Mrs Cripp saw the diary in the study and she informed Hannah what Phoebe was writing that Constance began keeping her own.

Phoebe lied and exaggerated everything but fortunately I was often with both Phoebe and Constance when things were alleged to have happened so things were not too bad for a while.

Chapter 13

I had by now deteriorated some fifty per cent but was holding on to the remainder fairly well. Constance, and Hannah when she was able to see us, helped no end. Even the grandchildren realised the importance of talking to me and asking me to do things.

'What's this, Granddad?' Or, 'What's that?' They were always showing me something like an apple or a shoe. They really did try to help me. I suppose I could have settled for that, just to have this part of my family and Constance putting up with the forgetting where I was, who they were, where I lived and setting off to see my mother and father. However, the foul language and the violence had become more frequent and I knew deep down they were all worried that I would do something to the grandchildren. Thankfully, as far as I know I never have.

Phoebe got rid of me for at least five days a week and there was a good chance it would become full time as she had already approached Constance on the subject. But then the worst possible news came: Constance's aunt on her mother's side was taken gravely ill and it was essential that she went over to America where the aunt lived to sort matters out. The woman was not expected to live more than a few days and as Constance was the aunt's closest living relative she was required to do certain things, particularly because her estate was substantial. Looking back, I suppose it was totally selfish of me, but the fear of not having her around sent me into a flat spin. She was my life, my reason to keep going, my protector and the only real love I ever had.

'Come on, David, be brave for me; it will only be for a few days and you know I would take you with me if I could, but they won't let me,' she said, trying to give me some crumbs of comfort from this dreadful situation.

Her flight from Manchester was only three days' away and during those three days I never left her side. I know I was like some little child clinging on to its mother, trying to stop her from being taken away from me. She never stopped reassuring me, she never stopped holding me and she never stopped looking at me and in those eyes I could see and feel her desperation too.

On the last night I remember neither of us slept and I know I held her so tightly, she was almost bruised by the morning. That dreadful morning, Hannah had volunteered to come with us to the airport. The taxi, with John its driver who we had known for years, arrived and we set off to the airport with Constance holding on to me as though we were locked together. Her smile could not belie the worry she felt in leaving me. We asked John to wait until I returned and then he was to take me back home. Why I called it home I will never know as I looked on Constance's house as my home, but I was to go back to stay with Phoebe while she was away.

Hannah stayed with the taxi while I gripped Constance's case, as if determined not to let it go. We walked into departures, not a word having been spoken throughout the whole journey, and even now I could hardly speak as the lump in my throat seemed almost to block the airways. Constance checked in and then we had two hours to wait before her flight left, spending the entire time sitting opposite each other in the café, drinking endless cups of tea while waiting for that dreaded announcement that Flight 701 to Chicago was ready for boarding.

Hannah had left us alone, not because she was helping her father have an illicit affair, but helping him to have love and security he so desperately needed. I could now see her deliberately sitting out of sight, but failing miserably, as I could see her taking a peek round the pillar to see if all was well.

'Flight 701 to Chicago boarding now.' That bloody announcement came sending shivers down my back. Constance put her arm tightly round my waist and walked with me slowly to the gate.

'Be brave, darling, for me, because I can't bear to see you like this and I need you to be strong. It is only for a few days. I promise.'

We kissed for what seemed like hours and yet it was the shortest moment of my life. Then our touch parted as we gradually let go of each other and Constance walked down the corridor, turning every few yards to stand and stare and wipe the tears from her eyes. Then it was all over, she had disappeared from view. I hadn't the chance to become lost or confused as Hannah took my arm.

'Come on, Dad. I've got you.'

'What on earth are you doing, David? Do you know what the time is?' The night sister asked rhetorically. 'It's three o'clock in the morning. You can't go wandering around like that.'

I was so distressed with my thoughts I just had to get up. I was walking round and round just talking to myself and thinking about what had been. Saying goodbye to Constance had been so stressful it made feel completely lost. In my head I knew I had to get back to her and I wandered off, but of course I could not find my way out.

The nurse took my arm and led me back to my bed and stayed with me until I had gone to sleep, but even when I woke up again I began to think about Constance leaving.

I remember Hannah and I watched the plane until it disappeared from view, or at least until it disappeared from my imaginary view, and then after one last cup of tea she took me back home to Phoebe's.

I had been amazingly controlled and seemed to have mustered

all my energies to remain compos mentis – that was until we arrived at the house.

'Dad's here, Mother,' Hannah shouted, trying to attract Phoebe's attention.

'Do we know how long she'll be away?' Phoebe asked.

Hannah answered for me; I couldn't remember what I had been told. 'Hopefully just five days.'

'It better not be longer; I don't want your father here for too long.'

'Mother, don't be so bloody wicked.'

'You don't know what it's like to have him around all the time.'

'Jesus Christ, Mother, you get worse. He's been good to you all these years and you have always made his life a bloody misery. He never had a chance.'

'He's made my life a bloody misery.

This became a heated argument between the two of them and my brain shut off. The next thing I remember was Hannah coming into the lounge to say she was going and would see me tomorrow.

This was the beginning of the end as Phoebe decided to take revenge for Hannah's outburst. She called in the support of my carers, or nurses as Phoebe preferred to call them, and told them I was not allowed out of my room unless she said so.

Unfortunately, once again I was not in a position to answer back and had to take whatever was thrust at me, even down to the removal of my privileges, as Phoebe began to call them, things like the removal of my magazines and newspapers. My reading ability was fast disappearing, but it was a force of habit to look at them, even if it was just the headlines or the pictures. She doomed me to sitting in my chair just staring out of the window and if it hadn't been for Teresa Wilson reading to me and having one of her wonderful but nonsensical conversations with me, I would have become a cabbage quickly.

Hannah came to see me every day with all the stories about

her family, the children, what they had been doing and telling me what was happening at Pennington's. Even though she stayed over an hour it wasn't enough for me, but she had her family to look after as well as a demanding job. I had been worried about her husband when they were first married, but surprisingly he became the housewife and looked after the family and they seemed happy enough with the arrangement.

I vaguely remembered Constance had promised to write and after a few days without any news it began to affect me; I couldn't get it out of my thoughts.

'What's the matter, David?' Mrs Cripp asked, seeing my obvious distress as she brought me in some tea and toast. I couldn't answer. 'Come on, David, try to tell me what the matter is.'

I managed to utter half the word 'Const. . .'

'Are you missing her, then?'

I tried to answer but the brain wouldn't allow it, but I know she could see it in my face.

'She's a cruel bitch,' Mrs Cripp whispered to Teresa, who nodded her acquiescence.

'David, you've got to eat something,' Teresa said.

Later that morning Mrs Cripp came hurrying into the room with a torn up piece of paper. Phoebe had intercepted the postman and tried to destroy Constance's letters to me.

From then on, between them they tried to intercept them before Phoebe got the chance to destroy them. Even then she asked them if there had been any letters from America for Mr Stephens. Mrs Cripp said, with an innocent tone, that she thought that Phoebe wouldn't mind her giving them to me, and Phoebe had to agree or face embarrassment.

The most dramatic argument came after about a week when Mrs Cripp and I heard Phoebe talking to Constance, who had rung to see how I was, and of course she was in full flow.

'Constance, darling, how nice of you to ring. He's fine, he's sleeping at the moment, and I'll tell him you rang . . . Later this afternoon perhaps. He's been very tired you know.'

Mrs Cripp raced down stairs and shouted to Phoebe, 'He's fine, he's awake,' making sure that Constance would have heard and putting Phoebe in a somewhat embarrassing position. By this time I was at the top of the stairs and could see the thunder on the Dragon's face as she had to add, 'Constance, we're in luck. David is awake now and on his way to the phone.'

I shuffled into the study with Teresa helping me and sat listening to the wonderful music of Constance's voice. She talked to me for well over half an hour, still with the questions and answers, and still with so much love in her that I could feel the pain of longing for her.

I couldn't talk too much but by the time we had finished I was a little better. She promised to phone me every day.

Both Teresa Wilson and I got the gist of the heated discussions between Mrs Cripp and the Dragon.

'How dare you interrupt me when I am on the phone? I will decide whether or not Mr Stephens can speak to someone, not you. If you ever do that again you will be out of a job. Do you understand?'

'Now you look here, you stuck-up bitch. Don't you talk to me or threaten me like that. If it wasn't for David, none of us would be here. AND if you want to sack me I shall tell the press what you are doing to that poor man. AND you can think about this. How you tricked him that Josh was his! Yes, lady muck, I heard everything. He's always been good to you and look how you treat him. Now am I sacked, because the press will love this?'

Phoebe just walked away, fuming but unable to do anything about it.

Shortly after, one of the nurses, Helen Laycock, decided she had had enough of Phoebe's antics and told her to stuff the job and left, leaving a vacuum which Phoebe found difficult to fill, as her reputation in the nursing world left a lot to be desired. However, a few days later, after Phoebe had consulted with Dr Banham, we had a new youngish woman called Anne Rafferty. An Irish girl who had a touch of evil in her. I can't really think of the words to describe her, but she was different. Phoebe immediately befriended her, giving her little bonuses when she thought no one was looking, always referring to me as her imbecilic husband, or words to that effect, so much so Anne began to treat me with less respect every day. I began to get annoyed and lose my temper with her and throw things, which played right into Phoebe's hands as unbeknown to me, she told her doctor again that even with all the assistance, now that Constance was no longer available, she needed a rest. She told him that Nurse Rafferty had only been in the job for a couple of days and had already recommended I be taken into a home.

The good doctor also advised them to keep a note of all the incidents and, of course, any that occurred were spiced up to make them sound worse. The doctor thought they had enough evidence to move me to a home and he would see what he could do. It has always surprised me what money or the thought of having a large sum of money could do to a person and Dr Banham was no exception.

He became a regular visitor to the house, never actually dealing with my problems, but my name was often mentioned. I didn't realise that Doctor Banham was using the incidents in Phoebe's diary, which he had allegedly seen, to put together Phoebe's case and every time he came, cash transactions passed between them and then suddenly with no warning I found out that Phoebe had transferred me from Dr Thumpington my National Health Doctor to Dr Banham's list. I remember I wasn't capable of protesting.

It was a terrible thing to do but Mrs Cripp would listen in to every conversation and report immediately to Hannah. On one occasion she telephoned Hannah to warn her that she believed that they were planning to send me to a home as quickly as possible, before Constance got back and this was made easier for them when Constance told Phoebe that she would be delayed another week or so.

She had been away for two weeks and during that time the

Dragon had stopped me from receiving phone calls, on the pretext that I was too ill. She even stopped anyone, apart from Hannah, coming to see me. It was just fortuitous that one of the nurses, Teresa, was on my side and had given me some mail and had intercepted the odd phone call.

On one occasion when Constance telephoned, I knew Teresa was talking to her and heard her say, 'Please come back soon for David's sake.' But the Dragon heard about the call and the nurse was sacked immediately.

However, another nurse, Phyllis Baker, was truly on my side and contacted Hannah about her worries. It wasn't long before I heard her shouting at her mother in a way I had never heard the like before.

'What are you doing to my father is cruel, you bloody woman: not letting him take calls or having anyone read to him.'

'It's for the best, Hannah.'

'Only for you, Mother. You just want him out of the way and don't care if he ends up dying a miserable and lonely death. Well, he's not going to and I shall see to that.'

'Hannah, I won't let him take calls as he gets too upset, especially if they're from that woman.'

'You mean Constance, the only person from the very beginning that cared. You never did.'

'I think you had better go.'

'I will not. This is my father's house and I am going to see him.'

'Well make the most of it, Daddy's darling, because he won't be here for much longer.'

'Are you still plotting to get rid of him?' Hannah shouted as she made her way to my room.

'Hello, Dad,' she said as she came into my room. 'How do you feel this morning?'

I remember smiling, even more so when she squeezed my hand.

Phyllis Baker scurried in the moment she heard Hannah.

'He does know you; he's just having a bad day with all the trouble. Yesterday he was fine and could talk to us and walk around, but he's worried and misses Constance. We are worried Mrs Stephens is going to put him in a home and he's not ready for that yet. Your father still has long periods when he's all right and you would hardly think anything was wrong. But the pressure from Mrs Stephens is too much for him.'

Hannah stayed with me for a couple of hours giving me her latest news and it actually brought me round and I was able to converse with her. It was a wonderful respite from Phoebe's constant tirades. But then she dropped me another bombshell to add to the enormous crater I already had, by telling me she was about to go travelling to Europe for two weeks as Pennington's were taking part in a big exhibition in Paris and then Amsterdam. She would be away for fifteen days or so and threatened her mother that if I was not looked after properly she would sort her out on her return.

I could almost take everything in. On the one hand I was proud of Hannah for what she was doing with the firm for the business was very important to all of us, and of course it was wonderful experience for her. But on the other hand I was worried what Phoebe would get up to with neither Hannah nor Constance to protect me.

The next day, whilst all the staff were out, Phoebe had a visit from Dr Banham. It really seemed very cloak and dagger as every door was shut behind them so I knew something was afoot. I suppose they must have chatted for a good hour, before he came out and bumped into me.

'Hello, David. Are you OK?' he asked.

I wasn't able to answer, as I knew something was wrong and it had unsettled me.

Phoebe let him out and they shook hands.

'Don't worry we'll soon have everything sorted for you,' Dr Banham told her.

'Shall I talk to James?' she asked him.

'No, no,' he said quickly. 'Leave all that to me.' And with that he was gone.

Phoebe shut the door and was like the cat that had got the cream.

The following week we received a visit from what I thought was another doctor and for some reason I lost my means of communication. I could hear and understand everything but could not comment, which made me so frustrated it vented itself in anger and I rounded on the man. It was not his fault but it painted a worse picture of me than the reality.

'He's like this all the time,' Phoebe said, trying to gain his sympathy, and then the lies really started. 'He wanders off and we have to send parties to look for him. He becomes extremely violent and attacks me and now doesn't even know me. I can't cope with this anymore,' she continued, with crocodile tears beginning to fall.

'Don't upset yourself, Mrs Stephens, we'll look after him.'

'Thank you,' the Dragon replied, sobbing.

I remember the next few moments vividly; it was now like a comic cartoon as Phyllis my nurse walked in. The tears disappeared as Phoebe yelled, 'OUT,' gesticulating with a flourish towards the door. 'Don't you dare come in when I am in with my husband,' she continued to the obvious embarrassment of the man.

'I'm so sorry about that. You cannot get reliable people these days can you?'

The man shuffled uncomfortably as Phoebe's artificial calm returned. 'Now, when can you take him?'

'Oh, as soon as you wish, Mrs Stephens.'

'This afternoon?'

'Well . . . yes. If that is what you want?'

'The sooner the better.'

Well that was that; no sooner had the man gone, he was back, and I was hustled out of my room, carried downstairs and almost pushed into the back of a minibus. The Dragon had actually given all the staff the afternoon off and made it quite clear she didn't want them around. It was obvious to them that she was trying to get rid of me and was taking full advantage of both Constance and Hannah being away.

I did manage to see the name on the side of the minibus before I was locked away with my suitcase almost dumped on top of me by the bitch. Sunnyridge Retirement and Nursing Home – and judging by the van they took me away in, I knew it wasn't the best and by god I was right.

Chapter 14

After an hour's drive we arrived at the place as dusk was beginning to fall. I remember it didn't feel right and I shuddered as the van pulled up outside the door.

The building itself, at the top of a very steep hill, had originally been three large terraced houses. They had been knocked into one to form the nursing home. There was no front garden and the front door opened directly onto the pavement.

The door was opened by a foreign woman – the matron, Mrs Grice, I later learned – who came out all smiles like some cardboard cut-out from a Mr Smiley book; it was totally false.

'This is David. He's come to stay with us,' the driver Mr Hanks said. 'Come in, David, you're home now,' he continued cheerfully.

He turned out to be the driver, the odd-job man and the porter.

Anyway, they helped me out of the minibus. I could smell the sea and the thought of Constance came into my head, causing me to shed a few tears. I looked down the hill and I could see and hear the waves crashing against the breakwater. It caused a momentarily lapse of concentration until Mrs Grice said, 'Come on, David.'

'I don't want to stay here, this is not my home. I want to go back to my home,' I managed to say, which startled them somewhat.

'No you don't, David, you'll love it here.'

Mrs Grice opened the door and at that moment I could smell the place: it stank of wee and was certainly dirty. The moment we entered I wanted to put my handkerchief across my nose and mouth. The trouble is, when you believe you are fighting for survival, smells become less important.

'Hello, David,' Mrs Grice said, holding out her hand for me to take, which I ignored.

'He understands everything,' Mr Hanks whispered into her ear, not realising I was neither daft nor deaf.

'Oh, right then,' she replied, a little confused. 'Well, David . . .' she began in a patronising voice.

Why do these people talk to us in this way? Don't they bloody realise it is far better to treat us normally than put on this air.

Oh god, I've forgotten where I was . . . Oh yes, I had just arrived at that awful place and Mrs Grice, the matron, was welcoming me. Well, if you call it a welcome.

'We have reserved the best room for you,' she continued. 'It overlooks the sea and you get the sun all day. Now, we'll take you upstairs and get you settled in.'

'I don't want settling in. I want to go back home.'

'OK. First thing tomorrow we'll take you back, but it's a bit too late now,' she replied.

The clever psychological move worked. I succumbed and went with them. I walked through the place with the terrible smell well and truly up my nostrils, passing rooms where it was obvious there were terminal patients. We then passed the toilet where there were little pools of urine around the base. No one had made any effort to clean it up.

Every few seconds, as we passed one of the nurses, Mrs Grice would say, 'This is David; he's come to stay with us.'

The nurses would chime up with dutiful responses: 'Hello

David, I'm Sharon' or Letty or Pat and some other unpronounce-
able names. 'I'll see you tomorrow,' they'd say, as though they
had been programmed.

'You won't because I am leaving tomorrow,' I told them.

The nurses were scruffy and wore what they wanted rather
than a proper uniform. They were certainly not in the job for the
vocation; many were foreigners who could not speak English
properly nor understand what most of us wanted. I remember in
one of my good moments I asked Frieda, a Polish lass, what she
earned and was astonished to find she was paid below the
minimum wage and that the boss took out the cost of her meals
from her wage.

I could tell from the first few minutes in the place what I was
in for and it wasn't going to be pleasant.

'Here we are, David, here's your room. You'll have to wait till
tomorrow to see the view. You will not get a better one in any
posh hotel.'

God help the others if this was their best room.

You see, that was my problem, wasn't it. I had stayed in the
posh hotels. I had had the good life and I still could have it with
the right support. I resented this woman talking down to me but
it was Phoebe, the Dragon, who had put me in this position, it
wasn't their fault but it took a lot of biting my tongue to stop me
saying what I thought.

Oh yes, I remember that room. The cruel bloody woman. I had
given Phoebe everything she had ever wanted and now I was
dumped there. She hadn't even checked what the place was like;
it was all arranged over the phone. All they were interested in
was the fact we were wealthy and the money was ready and
waiting for them.

My room was very cramped and only just big enough for a
small single bed, one bedside armchair to sit in, a book shelf, a
small cupboard for my clothes, a television stuck on the wall and
a coat hook on the back of the door.

'Do you want anything to eat?' the matron asked as I looked around the 'luxury' of my room.

'No thanks.'

'I didn't think you would. Patients like to settle in before they get their appetite back. But I'm sure you'll want breakfast in the morning.'

I didn't answer, simply falling on to the bed, wanting to scream, and then my mind went again. They hadn't expected this, as I had been quite lucid, and it caused them some confusion. I had obviously been painted much worse than I really was. I soon found out it was better for them when I was loopy, as they called it, because they could do what they liked then, knowing that we would not understand, or at least thinking we would not understand.

'Take his clothes off quick and put him in his pyjamas. Put his clothes in his case and take them to the storeroom. Don't let him know where they are,' the matron instructed.

'Shall I take him to the bathroom?' one of the young ones asked.

'No. Put a rubber sheet on the mattress and bed him down quickly. Then put two of these pills in his tea and he will be no trouble until the morning.'

I could not resist and when she brought the tea and fed it to me, I drank it. I did sleep that night, but I also wet the bed, for which I was admonished and told if I did it again I would stay in it all day.

I stank like the rest of the place and had to stay wet in bed until I had eaten breakfast. No one could imagine what that was like and what was worse I could not remember how to eat or drink because I was too distressed. Ten minutes later the delightful but soon to be cruel nurse Pat entered.

'Don't you fancy breakfast then; not good enough for you? Well, we can't have that then, can we?' And with that she took the tray away and I was left with nothing to eat.

A few minutes later she came back with another younger woman.

'Now we are a dirty little boy today, aren't we? We've wet the bed and we are not going to do it again are we?'

I couldn't answer and with that they stripped the bed back, yanked off my pyjamas and left me lying naked on the rubber sheet.

'Don't you want to talk to us then?' she asked, and again I couldn't answer.

'Well, David, this is what we do to nasty little bed wetter's,' she said and flicked my testicles with a wet towel.

I screamed in pain and she simply shut the door so that others could not hear. I began to wee, which puddled on the rubber sheet and which, to her sheer delight made sure I was covered in it, before she left the room. It was well over two hours before she returned and I remember as she walked back in, I was still naked on the rubber sheet but I was now terrified of her, so much so I messed myself.

'You dirty little bugger, you're going to have to stay like that, until you learn how to behave yourself.' She made sure my lower quarters were covered in crap and then she left me again.

I was fortunate however as Phoebe had phoned to say she was bringing some more of my things over. It made them realise it was perhaps better to clean me up, but I was sure in my mind Phoebe wouldn't have bothered herself about how I was being treated. In fact, I think she would have gained a great deal of pleasure from seeing me like that, but within the hour of her call, my bed and bedroom was spic and span. I was washed and brushed up, put into the home's standard pyjamas and dressing gown and taken to the sitting room.

This was a delight. All the chairs were placed round the edge of the room and in each chair was a body. I can't say a living person as we all sat looking into space, not talking or acknowledging each other, simply staring. I am absolutely sure we were all drugged up with tranquillisers to make sure we didn't cause difficulties for the staff or each other.

Phoebe arrived and came into the sitting room and saw me there along with the others. We all looked dull and docile, but I had not eaten or drunk anything and therefore not drugged so I watched her as she made her entrance. Immediately I could see that supercilious smile on her face, the one which she always wore when she had got her own way or won the argument.

'Perfect matron,' she said as she saw my demeanour. 'I don't want him back' she whispered quietly to the woman.

I got up and walked over to Phoebe, my faculties returning a little.

'Get me out of this place,'

'Don't be silly, dear. You know I can't look after you.'

I didn't hear the rest as Pat had walked in and this set me off again.

'Don't worry, Mrs Stephens, he won't trouble you again,' the woman assured Phoebe. 'We have to make sure all these patients are locked in as they tend to wander off. Don't they Pat?' the head nurse said.

'Not on my shift,' she replied.

'Good, I am pleased about that; I really do deserve a rest,' said the Dragon.

'I'm sure you do, Mrs Stephens. Would you like to see his room?'

'No, I'm sure it's fine and I feel reassured now. He's all yours.'

I was taken back to my seat and told to stay there, but my brain was out of control so I was up again and began to wander. I could see Phoebe was delighted as Pat took my arm and told her that I would have to be locked in my room until I lost my wanderlust.

For a few minutes I just sat there unable to take anything in; even my normal sane thought processes had disappeared. There was nothing I could do and all I could think of was that I had been dumped in a nursing home in what appeared to be the dementia section, which was always locked with no chance for escape. I saw Phoebe give the matron and Pat a fifty-pound note each and then they all went out to have a little discussion.

I had several drinks during the rest of the day and it was quite obvious I had been tranquillised, so putting me to bed was easy and I did sleep without worries. However, the following morning I had wet the bed and once again I was tortured by Pat. It was a repeat of the day before. I was stripped off, flicked with a wet towel and left in my filth until midday, when I received another visit from Pat and the Polish girl. They did change my pants and simply stuck me in a nappy but not before playing with my genitals and making fun of me.

I was now docile and couldn't respond to anything except to do as I was told. I was helped to feed myself cornflakes with a very little milk, then bread and jam followed by tea and tranquillisers. Like a good little zombie I was taken to the sitting room where I was plonked in a chair between two senile old ladies and left, like them, to simply sit and stare.

This experience was one of the worst of my life. I had been dumped in what seemed like the poor relation of nursing homes where it was just a way of making money and few of the staff were really interested in the patients; as long as we were docile and subservient they were happy and as long as none of us caused them any trouble all of us were left alone. However, if one of us got out of line their patience would be stretched and we would all suffer.

It was a terrible situation to be in, particularly for someone like me who still had a mind that could at times be near normal, and so I could see and think about things I witnessed. What was even worse was that some of us knew things were wrong but couldn't react, both from the drugs and the fact our brains wouldn't let us. Some of the patients, however, did not know whether they were on this earth or fullers so I suppose it didn't matter.

What am I talking about? There I am arguing against myself.

Of course it matters what happens to those other patients, they also need to keep their dignity, whether they know it or not. And for those of us who can still think and reason, we need to see that they are treated with respect because we are worried about what will happen to us when we get worse. God I'm on my soapbox.

Where was I? Come on try and remember. Oh yes, I had been dumped in that hole. No, it was a sewer of a nursing home: Sunnyridge, and there was nothing sunny about the place.

I remember we were all left to sit round the edge of the room with no one saying a word.That's not entirely true. Some were talking, but absolutely incomprehensible rubbish. I just had to sit there watching my new world go by. I would study all the characters and watch their behaviour, like Clarence, who from his name you would think he was a gentle little chap, but not he. The moment his food arrived he would snatch it off the nurses and push it into his mouth as though he had not eaten for weeks and if he could, he would snatch everyone else's, particularly if he was released from his chair.

Then there was Mildred who would walk over to each person and shout,'Get out of my fucking chair.' Some would, some wouldn't, but she was at it most of the day. Harold, meanwhile, kept getting lost, even when he was in his room he would be lost. We would hear his pathetic little shout for help. The nurses would go to him and try to explain where he was but five minutes later we would hear it again, that is until they gave him some powerful sedatives to shut him up.

There was Brenda who spent the entire day shuffling from one door to the next looking for a way out. 'Is this the way out?' she would ask.

'No,' the nurse would reply, 'it's over there.' Then Brenda would shuffle to the other door, and then to another, and so on all bloody day.

Charlie and Wilbur had obviously been ill, one with a stroke and the other I didn't know, but both were plonked next to each

EDWARD EVANS

other in wheelchairs. They were incapable of sitting upright and one leaned one way and the other leaned the other way, both with their tongues hanging out. This was the source of great amusement for the 'carers' who would put them the other way round, facing each other, which made them look grotesque.

There were many others confined to wheelchairs and incapable of leaving them. I am certain they were not changed every day as I could remember what they were wearing the day before, and the day before that, and so they would smell of urine. The wheelchair candidates were always far too much trouble for the staff and were left to fester.

Jack Small was a bit like me; he still had the capability of reason and understanding and felt he should not be there. He refused to give in and would often go to the door and try to open it; when he couldn't he would kick the door and shout at the top of his voice to be let out. When the nurses came to control him, he would lay into them until the inevitable tranquilliser was administered and took effect.

I would have loved to talk with him, but he had only one topic of conversation: that he should not be in the home and the moment he began to talk about it, it set him off again on the long road to the next tranquilliser. I found out later from my friend Letty that he was eighty-seven years old and that his wife had died. For a short while it had upset his mental balance and like me with Phoebe, who wanted all my money, Jack's children wanted the same and so they too dumped him in Sunnyridge. They had now moved into his house and didn't even bother to visit him. He had been sectioned but there was no one to help him, not like my Hannah.

I remember on one sunny day Pat felt we would all feel better if we went outside and sat on the benches. I must admit it was a lovely moment away from the smells, but again we all sat staring into space, with the odd nurse or two ordered to stay with us to prevent us running away through the gate at the rear. It was a

190

hot day and in the full sun a little uncomfortable, which signalled the start of the 'fancy dress'.

Pat brought a large box of summer hats out for both men and women. Some were very nice and dignified, mine at least fell in that category but was far too big, but what made me so mad was there weren't enough men's hats to go round so some of the men had ladies' hats put on them. Some looked absolutely ridiculous, others simply stupid, some even tried to resist but they were forced to wear them. It was a disgrace and what made it worse was that some of the nurses, led by the evil Pat, made fun of the men and even took photos to put them on the wall of their office.

Irene, the woman I seemed doomed to be sat next to, had a beautiful hat that at least made her somewhat presentable and she was complimented by the nurses. In fact it was quite funny for when we were eventually taken back inside, she had had so much flattery she refused to let go of the hat and we had quite a scene. It was only when she went to bed that they were able to get it back.

These were my only contacts with life and there was no way I could keep going without deteriorating fast amongst these inmates. It was a cruel and terrible place. I could still just about read, but wasn't allowed a newspaper. Sometimes I was well enough to have a conversation, which was good for my brain stimulation, but no one would talk to me. Well, there was one nurse who would, Letty, but only when she thought she was not being observed. Sometimes when we had been talking in my room, she would hear someone coming and put her hand over my mouth to stop me from talking so no one would find out. I'm sure she hated seeing me sedated because I could feel her sympathy for me, and an element of resentment at my treatment.

Then, of course, there was Pat, the cruellest of them all. We all were frightened of her because if we did anything wrong we would be punished. The saddest aspect of this was that some of us didn't know we had done anything wrong so didn't understand.

The other more junior nurses would often try to emulate her behaviour to show off to the others. Their behaviour was often more extreme and even Pat would sometimes have to call a halt to their antics. The men suffered more than the women but we all had to watch our steps. I was just thankful I had someone – Letty – in my corner who I thought was fighting for me.

There were frequent humiliations. I remember a nurse coming across and saying, 'Come on, David, let's change your nappy.' Just a few months ago I would have blasted the nurse for shouting that, but with the tranquillisers I hadn't a chance. I was lifted out of the chair with the aid of another nurse and shuffled across the room to the toilet. The drugs also seemed to restrict my movements and I was now walking like a very old man. Once there I was put on the floor, where my dressing gown was used to mop up the urine, and they changed my nappy as though I was a baby. No one can imagine how embarrassing it was for me or how I felt.

The third day things started better, I hadn't wet the bed and didn't get punished, in fact Pat simply ordered that I had a clean nappy and clean sheets.

'See, David, that's what you get when you are a good boy,' she said, then turning to Vladys, the Polish girl, and whispering: 'His wife is on the way. Make sure he drinks all his tea; every drop.'

Sure enough breakfast arrived and I began to eat scrambled egg on toast, which wasn't too bad, but I deliberately left the tea. Vladys, however, had other ideas.

'You must drink your tea, David.' She put the cup to my lips but I turned away. 'Come on, David, you don't want to upset Pat, do you?'

That did it. I had lost all my confidence; I had no will to fight that woman and drank the tea.

It was the same routine as Phoebe's previous visit. My room was cleaned and I was taken to the sitting room and sat between the two women. Then to my horror when Phoebe waltzed into the room, I recognised her, but couldn't even get up. The tranquillisers had worked I was totally dependent on assistance and did exactly what I was told, like some aged automaton. I could see her as I stared vacantly into space and I could understand everything she was saying, but could not react in any way. I remember wondering what she had come for. Was it simply to check whether her little plan was working or to put some other Machiavellian one into operation.

'This is excellent,' she said, turning to Pat who had accompanied her in. There were about twenty of us just sitting round the edge of the room. What was excellent about that? Anyway, I remember after a few minutes of chat they came over to where I was sitting.

'Mrs Stephens, this is Irene and this is Deirdre, David's new friends. Aren't they, David,' Pat said, once again in her patronising voice. 'You like to sit with them don't you?'

Yes, of course I do, like I like a bloody hole in the head, I thought, but couldn't say aloud. They never stop talking. They are so interesting, they're so up to date in their political thinking. Are you bloody stupid? Of course I don't like sitting with them, do I? But I have no bloody option.

Deidre suddenly spoke, 'What the fucking hell do you want. Fuck off and take him with you.'

'Deidre was the headmistress of the girls' grammar school,' Pat went on to say to Phoebe as they moved away.

'Irene is a different kettle of fish,' Pat continued, 'she was happily married with two children, but now she has gone into her shell and says very little. She is in the middle to late stages of dementia and no one ever comes to see her and like most people here, she simply eats and sleeps.'

I thought she had been a smartish woman in her time; her clothes you wouldn't call cheap, but the way the staff had dressed her and combed her hair the wrong way, she couldn't look presentable.

I'm sure Phoebe could see the sadness and desperation in my

eyes and deliberately picked up my hand, resting it on Irene's. 'I'm so pleased for you, David, that you have new friends and I'm pleased you are being well looked after.' She paused. 'Pat dear,' she said turning to her, 'this is just what I wanted. It's perfect.' She then put a fifty-pound note into her hand.

'You can visit him any time you like and if you have any problems just come and see me,' Pat told her.

'Oh I'm sure he will be fine. Anyway, I'm going away for a few days for a well-earned rest. Thank you. 'Bye David . . .'bye Irene. Look after him won't you,' she said, the sarcasm oozing from her. With that she was off. The bloody Dragon knew that would hurt me and I could see it in her face. She stopped in her tracks, had a quick chat with Pat, and walked back over to me and suddenly announced, 'Irene can be your new Constance, can't she, David?'

I knew then she was up to her old tricks. The mere word Constance I could remember, but in my present state, nothing else would register.

I was left there between the two women, Mrs Quiet and Mrs Fucker, the latter accosting me every time I moved, with her regular well-known phrase, 'Where the fucking hell are you off to?' and the former staring into space, with my hand still on hers. I couldn't move; it was as though my muscles wouldn't react to what my brain wanted so I just sat there.

The next thing I remember was a new voice, it was Sharon. 'You're a fast worker, you've only been here two minutes and look at you. Now, David, you leave her alone.'

I didn't know what the hell she was talking about until I realised that Irene was now actually holding my hand and smiling.

She was in a better situation than me as I was not allowed to wear my own clothes and was left in the nursing home pyjamas and dressing gown with the home's name duly embroidered on them. It was obvious they didn't want me to leave.

Lunch was now being served and we were shuffled along to

the tables at the other end of the sitting room, where we were given the most appalling rubbish known to man. The pudding, however, was not too bad, so I ate that. Fortunately, I could feed myself so at least that was one thing in my favour.

The inevitable cup of tea contained more sedatives so they were able to keep me under control.

After lunch Irene took my hand once more and we were led back to our seats. I observed that the television was still on. In fact, it was never switched off. The more I think about this the more I realise it was just background noise as none of us watched it.

At teatime, when I was back in my room, the door was unlocked and one of the Polish girls came in with tea and sandwiches. I didn't want to drink the tea but I was thirsty and needed a drink. My brain on the one hand was telling me that it was drugged but on the other it would not respond, and when the girl realised that I needed to be encouraged, she made sure I drank every bit of the tea and that was that. I was theirs hook, line and sinker.

The next day followed the same pattern, except that it was a glorious day and I was allowed to sit on my balcony. It was wonderful to watch the passers-by, to look at the sea and simply breathe in fresh sea air. It was however ruined when one of the nurses brought Irene to sit with me.

'Pat tells me you and Irene have hit it off,' the nurse said, 'so I have brought her to be with you.'

Take the bloody woman away, for Christ's sake, I thought. Oh why can't I talk sense?

'Come on, Irene, sit here next to David, he will look after you, won't you David? She needs someone like you to look after her, doesn't she?'

Irene did as she was told and we both sat on the lovely garden seat on the balcony.

I remember falling asleep and being woken up by the tyrant Pat. 'Would you two love birds like some lunch? I'm sure you would but we are going have to sit in the dining room. So, come on, David, stand up and help Irene, she needs a big man like you to help her. Well done, David, you are chivalrous.'

I felt good with all this praise, but of course it was their twisted psychology working.

We shuffled into the corridor and made our way to the dining room, in a different section of the home. This was a treat, I didn't realise there was anything like this.

'Come on, David, hold her hand and look after her.'

Neither of us knew entirely what we were doing, but we dutifully walked hand in hand through the normally locked door, along the corridors and into a large room where some of the other patients were already sitting at a table and eating. Some were even talking as you could hear the sound of their chatter as you entered. And then there was silence as they all turned to look at us, wanting to know who we were.

'This is David,' Pat said to the assembled company, 'and this is Irene, his lady friend.'

We were sat down next to each other and helped with our lunch. After we'd eaten, we were taken to another large room where we sang and played games and some people even danced to the music from a CD player. This was obviously the retirement home section of the home as everyone seemed compos mentis. I was encouraged to dance but the drugs would not allow me to move properly.

After a game of bingo we were taken back to our own section and left to resume our position in the sitting room. Once again I was sat with my hand on Irene's as someone had put it there.

I had come round a little and began to wonder why they were so keen to put us together and a couple of days later I found out, but not before I was out of it again. I had been well and truly drugged when Phoebe arrived, and was purposefully sat next to Irene and made to hold her hand. Phoebe came over and stroked Irene's head and then mine saying, 'I'm so pleased for you, David. You look so happy.'

We were joined by Pat, which sent me into overdrive, fearful that I might do something wrong.

'What time will they be here?' she asked Phoebe.

'In about half an hour,' the Dragon replied.

Who's coming? What she up to? God why can't I do something? Why can't I say something? Please let me say something. But it was impossible. I was full of god knows what, just sitting there with my hand on Irene's, which to the delight of the Dragon she was holding on to. I didn't have to wait long to find out what she'd arranged.

'Mrs Stephens.' Phoebe turned round. 'The doctors are here.'

'Oh good,'

'Good afternoon, Mrs Stephens, I'm Dr Wallace, the GP for the area, which of course includes this home. This is Professor Walter Milburn of Hull University and this is Dr James, he is a specialist in dementia. Now, shall we go into the meeting room and have David come with us?'

'Yes, that would be better,' Phoebe replied, and then promplty burst into tears.

'I know this must be very distressing for you,' Wallace commented.

'Yes it is. We have been married for a long time. Wonderful years.'

'Yes, I'm sure.'

I could hear this absolute crap emanating from her mouth and could not believe it. I think I wanted to kill her, or at least do something just to let them know the truth, but I was one of the zombies and had no chance to make my feelings known. I just had to take what was coming.

'Come along, David,' Pat said as she helped me out of my chair and as if it was pre-ordained bloody Irene would not let go of my hand, in fact Pat suggested that she be allowed to come along too. They all agreed, especially when she added 'I think they are fond of each other in their own little way.'

The look on Phoebe's face said it all. She could not have

planned it any better. She was once again the cat that had the cream. She knew she had won whatever she was planning.

The meeting room was a wood partitioned section within the sitting room. It was tastefully decorated with the usual chocolate-box pictures and within it there was a large boardroom-style table with eight chairs around it. If you sat close to the partition you could hear every word that was said, so there was no privacy, but I presume that because we were all suffering from dementia they thought no one would understand what was going on.

We were then sat down at the table and then the penny dropped, she, the Dragon was getting me certified and I could do nothing about it.

I can't remember who asked what, but the gist of it was I couldn't answer anything with all the tranquillisers inside me. Pat asked me if I knew who this was, pointing to Phoebe. Of course I bloody knew, but I couldn't answer.

The crafty bitch then asked me if this was Constance, pointing to Irene and the mere mention of Constance confused me, causing tears to fall, which were interpreted just the way the bitch wanted them to be. Then, whilst I was confused, she stuck the knife in and asked if I was fond of her and again I thought they meant Constance and made noises of impatience.

'He can't remember anyone. He only has his Irene now,' Pat added bringing the focus back on to me.

The tears flowed down my face like rain, I had lost and I was lost.

However, I did think I had a chance when the professor asked what drugs I was taking. I hadn't a clue and just listened. Pat replied that they had had to give me a double dose of tranquillisers as I could become very violent, and assured him that all members of staff could confirm this. She went on to explain how I get aggressive with the staff, throw the cutlery and plates off the table and even kick the furniture over.

'He is very strong, you know, and on one occasion it took three of us to restrain him,' Pat said. 'It really isn't fair on the staff so we do have to tranquillise him. It's strange,' she continued, 'when he's with Irene he becomes very calm and although they have only been together for a short time there seems to be a chemistry between them, She is a good influence on him.

'Do you know, the other night we had to put them together. He was sitting on the other side of the room and became really angry when he saw Irene opposite him.'

She's a bloody liar! Can't you see by just looking at me I wouldn't do that? I don't know what she is trying to do and where she gets these bloody stories from, but I've got to give it to her, she nearly had me convinced. Why is it when I have stress I lose it all and that is just the time when I need to be able to defend myself.

Of course I couldn't do the tests, I was drugged up to the eyeballs. The dragon was enjoying every minute of my discomfort. I failed everything miserably and there was no way in my present state I could do anything properly, which fell straight into her open arms.

I was then given a full physical examination.

'You're still quite fit, David. Your heart's good, your blood pressure almost normal, and you seem very well physically,' the doctor said as he examined me.

I was surprised that the blood pressure was near normal as I had always thought that under stress it rose. My luck was not in and even this simple examination was turned to Phoebe's advantage when Pat added, 'This is what I mean, he is very fit for his condition and is very strong, we do have to very careful with him.'

I then saw the knowing smile that passed between her and Phoebe.

The examination had finished and I was led back out into the sitting room and like a trained monkey, Bloody Irene was unhappy that she was not with me and made a fuss.

'Come on, David, wait for her, she needs a big man like you to look after her. See what I mean, doctor?' He nodded.

I waited like a well-trained dog in the middle of the room.

My mind was working but the brain and the body were weak. I knew what I wanted to show the doctor, but all he and that supercilious bitch could see was me waiting for Irene's outstretched hand. No matter what I did or what I thought, everything was going Phoebe's way.

I did think there was a possible chance of salvation when the doctor said as he was leaving, 'I'd like to come back in two days' time to see him again, try and avoid the tranquillisers.'

'Yes Doctor,' Pat replied.

'When will you be here?' Phoebe asked, fearing she might fall at the last fence.

'Thursday afternoon, about three o'clock.'

'I need the matter resolved as quickly as possible. We have a factory with eighty employees and I need to ensure the financial stability of the place, the workforce is depending on it.'

'Yes, of course. Pennington's isn't it?' he said, but she didn't respond.

What was the matter with them? Are they all stupid? How is Pennington's managing at the moment; how had it been managing in all the time I hadn't been able to work? Couldn't they see she was lying again? She'd never had anything to do with Pennington's. Oh for god's sake. Someone, please. But it was no use, I had lost.

'Have you finished with him now, doctor?'

He nodded and with that Pat turned to me and said 'Come on David hold Irene's hand,' and returned us to our chairs.

'It is lovely to see him looked after so well and with a friend. I can tell he is fond of her,' the Dragon said.

'Don't you have any regrets about this, Mrs Stephens?' the Professor asked.

'Of course I do. He was my whole life and we had a wonderful time together before he was ill. But . . .' she paused for effect and possibly to think up her next line, 'he hasn't known me for some time. He is violent towards me. I know it's not really him, it's his illness but it's still upsetting. He is now in a world of his own and I just want the best for him. You can see he is happy with Irene, that's lovely, isn't it? I want him to be happy.'

'Yes, you're right, and that is a positive attitude, Mrs Stephens.'

Right my arse, where's the violins? She just wants to get rid of me and where the bloody hell did she learn that script? Christ I couldn't believe it.

They continued to chat for several minutes, but unfortunately they closed the door and as I was back in my chair I couldn't hear anything. However, it was pretty obvious that Phoebe was getting her way as they all came out smiling. She then walked over to me, accompanied by Pat and the local doctor, took my hand and with tears in her eyes whispered. 'Goodbye, darling. I'll see you soon.'

Oh my god, she's at it again, where's Cecil B. Demille? He must be here somewhere, she could not have thought this up on her own. Can't you all see she's pulling the wool over your eyes? She's never called me 'darling'. Can't you see she's just a greedy little bitch? Then I remembered what I had done and burst out laughing, but even that was taken as though I was having a turn. She then turned to Irene and added, 'Look after him won't you?'

Pat played along with this, especially whilst the doctor was around.

'He took her to play bingo yesterday, didn't you David?'

I didn't answer.

'We thought we would take them into the main lounge, but it was too much for him. Well, for both of them really. They love sitting together holding hands and this morning they sat out on his balcony for a couple of hours. You could tell they were happy, they were just smiling.'

'Well, I must go,' Phoebe interrupted. 'I have a long drive home. Thank you, doctor. I appreciate your time.'

'That's fine. You've no need to worry, we'll have it sorted out for you this week, I'm sure. Will you becoming on Thursday?'

'Yes, of course. Goodbye,' and with a quick wave to me she was away, slipping Pat and the matron another hundred pounds.

I remember sitting there wondering what was going on and knowing there was a conspiracy to get me sectioned, to have me locked up for ever. Not only that, they were involving Irene in the scheme, brainwashing me as quickly as they could to make out we two poor old dears had a liaison going on. Oh isn't it sweet? He doesn't know anyone or want to know anyone other than her. That's why they kept putting us together. It appeared that Irene was a stage prop, something to make the whole thing seem real, but I couldn't help wondering what kind of sinister act they were playing. What was it all about?

The next two days were much the same. I could feel my brain slowing down even further and once again Irence and I were put out on the balcony in the sunshine together and allowed to go to sleep, only this time they took a photograph of her leaning on me. We were both smiling, God knows why, and of course they showed it to everyone, as though our relationship was special. I knew deep down that it was simply to show the doctors the next day but still didn't understand why.

The problem with a condition like mine was that there were days when I couldn't remember anything, so it was very easy for them the insert things in my memory: to make me want to hold her hand, to make me feel like it was normal to have her around, and I began to do just that. I even think they deliberately stopped me becoming involved with others to make me slow down. I think with the lure of Phoebe's bribes, everything was possible.

The fatal afternoon soon arrived and we were placed in our chairs awaiting the doctor's arrival and sure enough, he arrived on time along with some others but surprisingly Phoebe was late.

They took me to the meeting room on my own and began questioning me. I had some of my faculties back and began to respond, not properly, but a little better than before. They mentioned Constance, which sent me into sad mode and I began to cry saying that I wanted her, but they thought that I meant Irene and brought her in. I knew then I had had it. After they had taken several samples of blood Pat came in and apologised for interrupting them, but she felt I needed to go to the toilet with the result I was whisked off by Mrs Grice and Pat and given a quick-acting tranquilliser, which put me back in dream world. I knew what they were doing: the blood samples would show that I was clear of drugs. I was so confused when I returned I didn't make sense of anything. I was placed in my chair next to the woman of my dreams, or should I say nightmares, and had to listen to questions and mumble nonsensical answers.

Phoebe arrived apologising for being late and was greeted by the local doctor. I heard and understood everything.

'We have examined David fully and I am afraid that we consider he will never be able to make decisions for himself again. In view of the statements we have received from the home and from yourself, and from our own investigations and examinations, we feel he will not only be a danger to ordinary people but also to himself and therefore should remain in a secure environment.'

'Oh poor David,' Phoebe replied, sobbing with a sincerity that would impress Sarah Bernhardt. 'Well, I understand it is for the best that he stays here and at least he seems to have someone he can share his life with.'

'I just want to go over a few points with you, Mrs Stephens, before I go. All the appropriate papers will be with you in a few days. David will not be allowed out of this establishment without the approval of the doctors, unless he is transferring to another secure establishment, and that must also be approved.'

They mumbled a few other things and then he said, 'I must be going now. I'm so sorry, Mrs Stephens. I'm sure it took a lot of courage to do this, but you have done the right thing.'

'Well, David,' she said as she walked over to me. 'They have decided not to let you out again. So I'll see they keep you in the way you have become accustomed to. I'm glad you've got a new girlfriend.' She turned to Irene and kissed her on the head and once again said, 'Now you look after him for me, won't you?'

She looked at me and said, 'I wonder what Constance will make of this if she ever comes to see you. I'll tell her you have a new girlfriend. Shall I show her the photograph?' She then deliberately, for the second time, put my hand on Irene's, patted it, and then left me sniggering.

Chapter 15

I wish I could have told Phoebe what a heartless bitch she was, but the medication I was being given stopped being able to, so I just hoped someone would rescue me from the hell I was in. That, however, was beginning to be just a pipe dream.

After one of Phoebe's flying visits, I felt sure that she had warned the two women that Hannah would be calling to see me. I remember this because I heard them referring to her and from then on I felt everything was being done properly. Also, the doctor had made sporadic visits to ensure everything was in order from his point. Somehow, I was sure he was concerned for my welfare.

Within three weeks of entering the home, I had become a virtual cabbage. They had ensured I had had nothing to do, no one to talk to, and I had simply sat in a chair staring into space all day with the occasional sedative just to fuddle my brain and keep me compliant. From the moment the doctors had sectioned me, I was never free of drugs. I looked around for the first time comparing my lot with that of the others and I was sure there were several like me, where relatives had wanted to get rid of their embarrassments.

It was a simple form of euthanasia, in a way, or even legalised murder. They just left the poor sods like me with nothing of any description to do, heavily sedated, and the brain just closed down, and we died through lack of proper care. I was at the beginning of the end.

I was convinced there was a conspiracy to keep me in the place and that Mrs Grice and Pat were major players. They were doing everything possible to make me not only subservient and helpless, but also somewhat dependant on Irene. Phoebe must have told them about Constance and explained how fond of her I was so they probably thought it would be a good idea to have Irene's name associated with hers. For the next few days she made several visits to the place, but only to see the two women, probably to pay them, popping in to say a quick hello and to make a fuss of Irene.

But this I think was a mistake as they always referred to her as my Constance, so in the back of my mind, the bit that was still working, I still had the memory of Constance.

I was beginning to forget my family and friends even in the short time I had been there. Phoebe had certainly not told anyone where I was for I had no visitors. I had no discussions with anyone and just sat in silence all day, even the television was out of bounds.

I was sure I had been in well over six weeks when Hannah came. I remember there was a hell of a commotion and hearing Hannah shouting and swearing.

'I want to see my father and I'm going to see my bloody father.'

'You can't,' Mrs Grice said. 'He's having his medication.'

'I'll search every fucking room, if you don't take me to him.'

'Call the police, Pat. We can't have this, it will upset the others.'

'Call the bloody police if you like, but I am still going to see my father.'

She did try to get in but the door to my room was locked. The police duly came. Mrs Grice laid it on a bit thick about the way Hannah had behaved and as they were standing by the door I could hear everything.

'Now, come on, miss, what's your story?' the officer asked, having first heard their side of the story.

'My father has been taken from his home while I was away and brought here and they won't let me see him. It's taken me several weeks to find out where he is due to that criminal mother of mine not telling anyone.'

'Why not?' he asked.

'It's up to Mrs Stephens who knows,' interrupted Mrs Grice, 'but I would imagine it was to help him settle in, before being disturbed. It is the usual thing to do. As for the sectioning, it was for his own safety and that of others, so he is now sedated regularly. He becomes very violent if he isn't and upsets the other patients.'

'I don't believe any of this. I want to see him. If my mother, the bloody bitch, can see him, then so can I.'

'She can't,' said Mrs Grice. 'No one is allowed to see him.'

'That's not true, my mother told me she had seen him'

'She has, but not closely.'

'Then let me see him. Not closely,' she added sarcastically.

'I can't see anything wrong with that, madam,' the officer said and with that they opened the door to reveal me sitting next to Irene holding her hand.

'That's his new friend,' Mrs Grice said to the officer smiling. 'They are seldom apart and she keeps him calm.'

Hannah would have none of it. She raced across to me, flung her arms round my neck and hugged and kissed me.

'Dad, it's me, Hannah.' But I didn't respond. 'It's me, Hannah.' Again I didn't respond. She took hold of my face and looked into my eyes and said loudly. 'He's been drugged.' She then lifted my eyelids in turn and demanded, 'What have you given him; he's drugged out of his mind?'

'I've told you he has to be sedated as he becomes violent. We have to protect our staff. He is incapable of looking after himself and thankfully he has taken a shine to Irene which has had the effect of calming him down.'

'That's bullshit and you know it. I am going to take him away with me now.'

207

'You can't—' Mrs Grice began to say.

'You will need the doctor's permission to remove him from here,' the officer interrupted.

'Then give me the doctor's name and I will contact him. I will also stir up so much shit you will wish you hadn't been born. I'd like a few minutes with my dad and then I will go.'

'That can't do any harm, Matron,',the policeman said.

'Right, Pat, you stay with her.'

Hannah continued to hold me, promising she would have me out of the place as soon as possible. But it was more difficult than I had imagined. Phoebe was, after all, my wife and she had control of where I was to stay and what happened. It was the one thing I hadn't thought of when I made my will. Effectively I could remain in that place for the rest of my life, which is what Phoebe wanted. The nursing home did too, as it was very lucrative for them. Hannah being there, fighting my corner, made my mind active and I could think but not communicate these thought processes. However, I remembered the various aspects of my original intentions.

The fact that I had been sectioned could actually change the clauses of my will, so everyone had to be careful. I could remember that Constance owned my shares in Pennington's and could stop Phoebe's allowance straight away, but I'd lost Constance.

Pat was determined to show Hannah how I had changed and how I needed the new friend,

'He does need his new friend, Hannah,' she said trying to sound sincere.

'Bullshit, fucking bullshit and you know it. He's drugged up to his eyeballs and doesn't know anything.'

And then I played right into Pat's hands, Hannah took my hand away from Irene's and held on to it.

'She's his security blanket and he is hers. She is his Constance and we know how fond he was of her. It's just the same.'

'That's bullshit,' Hannah said but at the same time I took my hand away from hers and placed it back on Irene's, which she took and held on to,

'See what I mean,' Pat said, smirking. 'In the time he has been here they have become very fond of each other and it would be cruel to separate them now. They are in a world of their own.'

That was the clever psychology of what they had done, always coupling Irene with Constance's name. It made me want to hold her.

'My dad does have long periods when he is OK and god help you if I find out you have mistreated him or broken the law. Think on I know you have lied about his violence. I know he has been sectioned illegally and I am going to prove it. And bloody god help you when I do.' Her voice was so sinister that I even noticed Pat was concerned.

For the present Hannah realised that she was on a hiding to nothing and retreated. She left with a promise to get me out of there and that she would see her mother in hell for what she had done.

Hannah did see Dr Wallace privately and arranged that he should call three times a week at random, which was to include the occasional blood test. It did improve my treatment and conditions but Pat and Mrs Grice were clever, they would always make notes in the book that I had had a violent turn and had to be sedated. It did, however, cut the amount of sedation intake and this probably helped me a little. Later on Hannah told me she also discussed the relationship I was having with Irene and that I was often referring to her as Constance with Dr Wallace. He did say this can easily be induced into the memory when patients are drugged, and by always keeping us close together and always involving us in any activities together. It was a widely used trick but very difficult to prove it is done for ulterior reasons. However, he did promise he would keep his eye on things.

Hannah had obviously been busy trying to sort things out for me as we had an unexpected visit from Phoebe. I was still in my room when she breezed in along with Mrs Grice. They began by having a long chat about me as if I wasn't there and they both were under the impression that I no longer understood what was being said.

'Don't worry, Mrs Stephens. It will be all right; he will not leave here. He has been sectioned by three senior physicians and will have to remain until another place is found and as his next of kin, you are totally in control of that. It's for you to decide which is the best place for him, unless a medical condition is diagnosed, and that's unlikely. The more dependent he becomes, the harder it will be to remove him. This is one of the reasons we are trying to cement his relationship with Irene, she's has dementia but has some faculties left. She can understand sometimes, but not always. She is virtually in the same boat as he is. If we can get them walking round together and holding hands it makes a great psychological point. If we have visitors they will see them together and think it is just lovely and that they are happy. From the medical point of view it will appear they are settled and doctors are reluctant to move people when they appear contented and not troublesome.

'The only danger we have at the moment is that your daughter is employing Dr Wallace in a private capacity to keep his eye on your husband and she has also threatened to investigate the sectioning. So, the quicker we get him dependant on us and get the two of them closer, the quicker we can wean them off the sedatives, so even those won't trouble the doctor. It will also be unlikely they will wander off as they will want the security of each other.

'It's now purely a psychological game, which needs to be played carefully but quickly.'

I just listened, I could not believe what I was hearing as it confirmed that it was a conspiracy and I had no chance of fighting it. I hated that cow but could do bugger all about it. I just had to sit and listen to everything they said as they plotted my downfall.

'What can I do to help?' Phoebe asked.

Not a lot really, we will keep them together as much as possible and let them sit out on the balcony together. If you come to see him, bring something for her too, involve her in the conversations. Let us know when you are coming and we will sit them together in the lounge with the others. Talk to them both and if there are any other visitors present, involve them. Tell them that you have been happily married and that it saddens you that he is in here, but you are relieved that he has made a new friend. They will think you are an angel.'

'I was hoping not to come so often, that's why he's in here.'

'I understand but it will only be for a short while. If you can't then we will do the best we can, but it would help. Just for two or three months, then it will be finished, and David will be our responsibility.'

Phoebe didn't bat an eyelid; she could not think that what she was doing was immoral and illegal. She was only interested in what she wanted for herself.

Their plan was put into action with a vengeance. Irene and I were pitched together all the time and they had now got me into the habit of waiting for her so that I was even the one to take her hand first. This pleased Mrs Grice as it showed her plan was working and she got us unwittingly to demonstrate it in front of Dr Wallace.

They had now relaxed my supervision and were even dressing me in my own clothes. This was a treat and it did make me feel better. I was even beginning to think. We were taken round to join the less senile on another section and took part in the singalongs, the painting sessions and even the dances. We had our meals with them and I chatted incessantly, but it was rubbish as I often repeated myself. We were also able to move around more freely as I no longer gave them trouble. I had become a good docile little inmate.

During the next few days we had glorious weather and I was asked if I would like to go to the beach and to my astonishment I answered, 'Yes please.'

It also caused consternation with Letty who had come to help.

'Would you like Irene to come with us?' she asked.

Again I answered, but this time I said, 'No . . . thank you.'

'Oh come on, David, she depends on you. Don't be mean. Let's take her too.'

I didn't answer and this was taken as a yes.

'Oh well done, David, let's go and collect her shall we?'

I followed Letty down the corridor and we collected Irene.

'We're going down to the beach, Irene, do you want to come? David is going and he wants you to come. Don't you, David?'

'No,' I answered.

Both Mrs Grice and Pat heard me answer which prompted one of them to remark: 'He needs a sedative.'

'Come on, David, Irene needs your help.'

And with that I took her hand and walked with her down the road to the beach.

Letty, a young pretty lass who I thought was perhaps the kindest of all the carers at the home, was very good, she talked to me incessantly. It was real therapy and I am sure she realised that I needed this sort of treatment just to keep me sane. I did answer her questions as long as they did not require more than a 'yes' or a 'no'.

We sat on one of the benches and for the first time Irene chatted to me and I her. None of it made any sense, but there we were talking away as though we were long lost friends, and I have to admit it felt absolutely wonderful. When it was time to move on, we were led shuffling along the front accompanied by Letty, still chattering to one or another. I didn't notice when it happened but Irene had linked my arm and we were walking like Darby and Joan. We were out at least an hour before we returned to a smiling Mrs Grice. Letty was full of it. 'You should have seen them walking arm in arm and chatting away to each other; it was lovely.'

'You've done very well, Letty. What did they talk about?' Mrs Grice asked with a little snigger.

'Oh it was just rubbish, but they were talking to each other as though they had known each other for years.'

'That's wonderful. You have done very well, Letty.'

So much fuss was made about this little event I knew there must be something sinister going on. I now recognised all the false praise, but Letty didn't. I was just thankful she didn't mention our almost one-sided conversation, but even so I found that my teatime cup of tea was drugged and I was back in never, never land.

For the next couple of weeks or so, life was very much the same. There were many more walks out and many more liaisons with Irene. It had now become a natural thing for Irene to link my arm when we were out. More importantly, I had had several visits from Hannah who would always take me away and talk to me on my own. Always it was the questions and answers, trying desperately to get my brain working again. She always brought newspapers and magazines and it was beginning to combat my inertia.

Then it was Phoebe's turn to visit and her company had the opposite effect. She would always insist that I was sitting next to Irene and always talk to us both. I never wanted to talk to Phoebe so I didn't and I can honestly tell myself that I did it deliberately.

Dr Wallace came to see me a couple of days after her last visit and was talking as he normally did, not expecting an answer. It was just a general one-way chat whilst he examined me. He put the thermometer in my mouth and then said, 'You have a lovely room, David; it's the best in the house. I bet you like it.'

Once again I astonished myself and him, when I removed the thermometer and replied, 'I want to go home.'

He was silent for what seemed like a minute or two and then added, 'This is your home now, David.'

I interrupted him as for the moment I had my faculties. 'No, it's not. I want to go home to Constance.'

We could hear Pat coming along the corridor so our conversation stopped.

'I'll talk to you later,' Dr Wallace said.

The moment Pat walked through the door, I was thrown back into a confused state, which also worried the doctor.

'Nurse Davies, I want you to look after David. I think he is developing a reaction to something. Keep your eye on him. I'll try and pop in tomorrow.'

After all this time I had now learned that Pat was Nurse Davies. This to me was the beginning of the change; I was without doubt given less and less sedatives, or just enough to control me, even if I had been difficult. But it was not enough to completely destroy the rest of my brain.

Mrs Grice called a council of war and invited Phoebe over to talk about the situation. They went into the meeting room and shut the door, but didn't realise I was not completely with the fairies and got up to go and listen to the conversation. I had, however, forgotten my friend who would not let me go. She was holding my hand with a grip like a blacksmith holding his hammer. She looked at me desperation in her eyes, and yelled, 'David,' which drew the attention of Nurse Davies, who came running out of the room to see what was going on.

'Look, that's what we want, look at her,' nurse Davies remarked to the others, who had followed her and then they went back inside. I walked with Irene to the room and sat down outside in the hope of hearing what was said.

'No one would part them if they saw them behaving like that,' Nurse Davies said as she shut the door.

The brain is a wonderful thing and I knew mine was going, but like anybody whose life is in danger there is a part of the brain which makes the will to survive paramount, and I honestly thought that this little bit of my brain was giving me the will to survive. I had to try and avoid the drugs and the only way I could do that was to be good in the eyes of the nurses, but I also had to try and keep active.

I had wanted to try and read, but the moment Hannah left they confiscated the newspapers she had brought and dumped me back in the sitting room with nothing. In the mornings I would be sat out on the balcony with nothing and just left to vegetate, or with the company of Irene. That was another problem, whilst they had been working on me to cooperate and had involved Irene, they had succeeded fully in every respect. She now wanted to be with me all the time and started to play hell if we were separated. If I was not around she would start looking for me. It was a shame the psychology had worked on her, as she was becoming totally dependent on being with me whilst my brain, even when under the influence of drugs, knew I wanted out. I knew though that the psychology was beginning to work on me too and it was something I had to resist.

I found out later that Hannah had made several visited to see Dr Wallace and he had become almost as worried as she had. However, he had advised her to play it cool as they did not want to create more trouble for me in the home or cause more drastic steps to be taken by the staff.

I did notice a more strange behaviour from her during her next visit. She arrived just as I was shuffling along the corridor with my friend who had linked my arm.

'They won't be parted you know,' Pat Davies said as she met Hannah.

'Mmm. It is cute.' Hannah added, 'I just want the best for him. He's my dad after all.'

'Of course he is and he is very special to you, but he is in the best place and if we can make him feel comfortable and happy we will. If he makes special friends and it makes his life easier, then it is the better for him.

'I see you've brought him the papers, Hannah, but he won't read them, I'm afraid. Can I call you Hannah?' she asked, sounding as though she had made a conquest.

'Of course you can,' Hannah replied. Then she turned to me. 'Come on, Dad, I'll take you to your room and we'll have a chin wag up there.'

Well, it was more difficult than I had imagined it would be, as that bloody Irene would not let go.

'I told you they were close and like to be together,' Pat said.

'I'll take her as well then.' And with that, Hannah, Irene and I made our way slowly to my room. Once there, the door was closed and the reason for Hannah's change of heart became apparent.

'Look, Dad, I hope Irene doesn't understand, so I am going to have to be quick. I will get you out of here.'

Those words returned some of my confidence which I had lost thinking she had given up on me.

'I want you to wear this watch all the time, don't take it off. Do you understand me? Answer me, Dad.'

I smiled and nodded.

Hannah put the watch on and then began to read some of the stories from the papers, involving Irene as well as myself, and this was either fortuitous or well planned on her behalf as Pat Davies came in to see if everything was all right and witnessed the cosy scene.

'I'm just reading them a few stories from the papers. Dad likes that.'

'I wish other people made such an effort for their families.'

'I owe him a lot, it's the least I can do. I'm going to bring my children to see him the next time, is that OK?'

'Of course it is.'

'Oh by the way, I've brought him his watch, he always loved wearing it. It is waterproof etcetera. Will that cause a problem?'

'No, not at all; anything to make him more comfortable.'

'Show Nurse Davies your watch, Dad.'

'It's lovely, David. You are lucky,' she said in that patronising voice of hers, which made Hannah wince. She stayed another half an hour or so and then walked me back to my chair in the sitting room, with her linking one arm and Irene the other. She kissed me goodbye and shook Irene's hand and left, promising to visit me again in a couple of days or so.

'You too, Irene,' she added.

I could hear the joyful comments from Mrs Grice, who had

just come on duty, and the loyal Pat Davies. It was obvious that were confident of victory.

The next few days were almost the same as previous ones. I suppose not much can change when nearly everyone is in a semi–vegetable state, except that Hannah had requested that Dr Wallace call on me every day, which put the home in difficulties and appeared to make the staff nervous. However, the good doctor, who, after my constant conversations, was now concerned about my being sectioned, had started his own quiet investigations.

He told the staff he was worried about my condition and blood count and was worried that the tranquillisers were having a bad effect on me.

'It's only when he becomes aggressive that we give them, doctor,' Mrs Grice said.

'How often is that now?' he asked.

'A few times a week.'

'Please let me know as soon as possible the next time he has a violent outburst. I want to see him on the next occasion before he is sedated. Can you do that?'

'Yes, doctor,' she replied.

'I want to try him on some different ones.'

Well, I didn't have to wait long until I was given a large dose which put me back days and the next thing I remember was the doctor examining me in the sick bay. There were broken glasses on the floor, my room had apparently been ransacked and I had even had a go at Irene. I was almost out of it, but I could still take in what was happening and I heard the incident book had been duly noted that I had been extremely violent and for my own welfare and all others on the premises I had had to be immediately sedated at 9.30 p.m.

The doctor noted all matters and arranged that I be taken away to hospital for examination as he was worried. The ambulance duly arrived and I was whisked off to the local hospital where I remained until all the drugs were out of my system.

Hannah came to visit a couple of days later having been told to stay away until Dr Wallace thought it was OK for her to come. She knew, however, what he was trying to do and that her visit was to coincide with the doctor's.

'You have certainly unearthed a can of worms, Hannah. I don't believe your father was in need of permanent care and certainly not in need of such strong sedation. However, I will deal with that and all I want you to do now is take you father out and get him some fresh air and see if we can get him better.'

'Where's your watch, Dad?' She said almost hysterical. Thankfully, it had been put in my cupboard when I was admitted. Not much was nicked from the geriatric ward as it was always locked, but it was back on my wrist in seconds.

'Don't let anyone take it off you, Dad,' Hannah ordered.

We took a lovely walk into the country with Hannah really trying hard to get my brain active, before she remembered the bit of good news she'd been looking forward to giving me.

'Constance is coming back soon.'

She thought I would be excited but I had almost forgotten her with all that had gone on and at present I had Irene in my mind whenever Constance was mentioned. Hannah could see the problem, fortunately, and worked on my mind like nothing else. She felt it was so important to me she even stayed overnight and the next day.

Doctor Wallace called in to see me in the afternoon together with James Percival, who Hannah had contacted for his support, She wasn't sure Wallace would believe her so asked James to tell him about Phoebe and what she had done. Wallace was very shocked. He tried to contact Professor Milburn and Dr James, who had sectioned me, but they were unavailable for a few days. Wallace felt it was essential that they were involved to ensure the sectioning was removed. In fact, all I could see him doing was protecting himself and his colleagues. The fact was I had been sectioned and Percival and Wallace thought it better if firstly I went back to the home as it was against the law to do otherwise.

Then they should attempt to get to the truth. James Percival emphasised that Phoebe should not be aware what's going on.

I knew I was better off in hospital, but beds were always wanted for more urgent cases and so I had to be shipped back to my Sunnyridge prison. But I knew deep down that it would not be for long.

It was strange going back. I had almost forgotten much of what had gone on. However Hannah decided to get the watch examined and took it back. I was amazed that as I walked through the door the first thing that Pat asked was, 'Where's your watch?'

I didn't know as I wasn't quite with it at the time, probably from the upset of being moved back there. In fact, it was at least a couple of days before I became aware of things again. I do remember one thing though, Wallace had instructed that no drugs of any description should be administered to me as I had been given some of the new drugs to stop my violent outbursts already. True to his word, the doctor visited me every single day with the result I was treated like royalty.

Chapter 16

After all the excitement and then a period of nothing, I eventually began to come round little by little. They had even been wheeling me down to the sea to get some fresh air, or I should say that Letty did. It was really her that improved my lot as she would talk to me, tell me what was going on and it was just me and her on the beach. There were times now when I could answer her and we could have an almost two-way conversation.

On the third day back Hannah came to visit me, mainly to return my watch for added protection, and for the first time she brought the grandchildren with her. God it was wonderful to see them, and boy did it bring my brain back to half power.

'Hello, Granddad,' Elizabeth yelled as she ran across the room to greet me, closely followed by Max, who was equally excited. Thankfully my shadow, in the shape of Irene, was not there and the chair next to me was vacant. Hannah sat down next to me with Elizabeth on her lap and Max sat on mine and we listened to the excited jabberings of the two most lovable kids in the world. It was wonderful to be able to speak to them, even if only slowly. We chatted about school, their friends, what they'd been doing, and then there was the inevitable question, 'When are you coming home, Granddad?' from both of them.

'Soon,' I replied, to my own astonishment.

Then we had several minutes of pure theatre as Irene returned to her chair. She was really angry to see another woman sitting next to me.

'David,' she shouted, once again drawing the attention of Mrs Grice and Letty, who came running over. The poor woman was going ballistic and no matter what they said or tried to do she was pulling at Hannah to go away. The children were terrified.

'Come on, Irene, it's only Hannah, David's daughter. She's not come to take him away. You don't have to worry.'

'Haven't I, Mrs Grice? Don't you be too bloody sure,' Hannah whispered in her ear as she got up to make way for Irene.'We know what your game is, and it's over, and if either I or the doctor find any more sedatives in my father's blood the police will be involved. Do you understand? Oh, by the way, see his watch? It's a recorder; this disc, it's recording everything that happens. Make sure it stays on him or I'll know it's been removed.'

Mrs Grice went pale; I almost thought she was going to faint as she stumbled to hold on to a chair.

'Come on, Dad,' Hannah said to me. 'Let's go to your room we can talk more easily up there.'

She took hold of the children and we walked slowly to my room with Irene bringing up the rear.

'And you can stop that woman following us; we don't want her with us.'

Mrs Grice took hold of Irene. 'You can't go with David, he has to see the doctor,' who, at that moment, announced his presence by walking through the door.

Again Mrs Grice was surprised as it was not normal for the doctor to arrive at this time of day. Pat also came on duty to be greeted by Mrs Grice and was obviously apprised of the situation, because she immediately telephoned Phoebe who arrived less than an hour later.

Doctor Wallace had left by then, so Phoebe took her anger out on Hannah and me.

'What do you think you are doing and what's this about a recording?' she asked.

'Mother, I said you were an evil bitch and you've proved it

221

and when people hear what the staff here and you have done to my dad, I'll be surprised if you have any friends left. Nor those brothers of mine, who haven't been to see him at all.'

'I told them not to as it would unsettle him. They also know how violent he has been towards me and all the trouble he has caused – and the fact that he is having an affair with Constance.'

'What! Are your stupid? You know that's not true.'

'Well, I don't care what you think, it's up to me whether he's moved and I don't want to be. He can stay here with his little friend and rot. Now, tell me about this recording you are supposed to have.'

'Take a look at that,' Hannah said, showing Phoebe my watch. 'A closer look, Mother.'

Phoebe looked at it from all angles, but couldn't see anything special about it.

'It's a digital recorder and lasts for days. On the one I've already taken home, you can hear the staff discussing deliberately drugging Dad to make out he has been violent.'

'Well, that's not me is it? Now, give me that disc and don't be so silly.'

'Mother, there are several copies, so there's nothing you can do.'

'Well, he stays here, whatever you say, and I will have a word with the matron.'

With that she stormed off to see Mrs Grice.

She obviously told them that I wasn't going anywhere and that I was here to stay, but even so my lot was improving by the minute.

Hannah had had enough of her mother and could not resist hitting her where it hurt most, that of the pocket.

'You know. Mother, you are in for a big shock when Constance gets back.'

'Why is that, dear, what on earth could Constance do to me She spoke in her usual arrogant tone.

'Who pays you a monthly allowance?'

'Pennington's does and will continue to do so. I now have power of attorney over his affairs so what can you or anyone else do?'

'That may be the case, Mother, but Dad doesn't own Pennington's.'

'I know he doesn't, Hannah, but we are the main shareholders so it is ours really. In fact, it's mine now,' she said haughtily.

I knew what was coming and I started to laugh as Hannah continued. 'No, we don't, Mother. None of us has any shares in Pennington's.'

'Who does then?' she asked slowly and deliberately.

'The only person who ever cared for him.'

'NO! Not Constance!'

'Yes, Mother, Constance.'

'You lousy miserable bastard,' she shouted at me, as by now I could not stop laughing.

'I shall contest that on the basis that his mind is gone; the man is an imbecile.'

'Mother, don't waste your breath He did it nearly fifteen years ago when things were normal and he was tested by many experts to confirm he was completely of sound mind and understanding exactly what he was doing, so I think you should consider your position very carefully.'

'You miserable old man, you would do this to me after all I have had to put up with!'

I found the power of speech simply to say the word 'JOSH'.

She fell silent and not another word was spoken. In fact she just stared at me for a few moments and then left, but she at last knew that I knew, she had tricked me into marriage and realised she that she was now facing the consequences of that deception.

I think she now realised that without a fight she would lose everything and the one thing you could say about her, was that she was a fighter. Hannah realised that her prime task was to get me out of the home as quickly as possible.

We had two choices, firstly Phoebe would have to agree the

transfer to another home a or, secondly, we had to get the sectioning order removed immediately. To do this we had to get the three experts who had been involved to change their minds. We knew Dr Wallace was on our side but were not sure what the reaction would be from the others.

Hannah didn't want to wait for them to set up a meeting and to arrange another examination, because my health would suffer every day I was left in the home. It took all of Doctor Wallace's powers of persuasion to make them change their minds, as members of the medical profession seemed reluctant to admit they have made a mistake. Even then they would only allow my release if I went to another secure establishment until the final paperwork was issued. It was just a formality but none the less I had to reside away from home for a further few days.

Terence, my solicitor, was persuaded to write to them explaining the circumstances and advised them that he would have their actions examined by the police. From that moment they moved with some purpose. I remember it only took a few days for the paperwork to come through for me to be released from the care of Sunnyridge.

Hannah arrived on the due day and then I was away. I felt dreadful that Irene had been put through the mill simply to get at me and I really did feel sad when I said goodbye. I could see in her eyes that she was unhappy and couldn't understand fully what was happening. I was operating at about thirty per cent and was able to say goodbye with a kiss, but it was her piercing shout 'David' as I went through the door which has haunted me ever since.

We met Mrs Grice and Pat Davies at reception where Hannah turned on them like a snake attacking its prey. I could almost hear the words hissing from her mouth.

'I've only just started on you two and I'll guarantee you'll spend Christmas behind bars.'

'It wasn't our fault, it was your mother's doctor. Doctor Banham, asked us to do it.'

'Did he pay you?'

'Yes,' Mrs Grice said.

'Then you and he will pay for it. Oh, and while I think about it, don't go down any dark alleys by yourselves unless you have to, until you send all the money that we have paid for his keep and torture. It will make a wonderful newspaper story, won't it?'

Hannah took out her phone and quickly snapped a picture of them both looking shocked.

'Don't forget what I said,' she added.

They looked on open mouthed as we made our way through the reception area.

'Come on, Dad, let me take you home.'

We opened the front door of the home for the last time allowing the fresh air to fill our nostrils and get rid of the stench and dishonesty of Sunnyridge.

'Can we go for a walk along the seafront before we leave, please?' I asked Hannah.

'Of course we can.'

We set off down the hill to the promenade and walked slowly along the front without a word being spoken. It was such a relief being free. We turned at the end of the prom and began to walk back when we bumped in to Letty.

'Hello, David, what are you doing here at this time?' she asked.

Slowly but surely I told her I was going home and then Hannah told her the story of what had happened.

'I knew you were somebody special and I loved to talk to you.'

'Thank you, Letty, for what you did for me. I won't forget you reading and talking to me.'

Hannah stepped in again and gave her a business card and said, 'If you're intereted in a full-time nursing job looking after my dad, give me a ring.'

We left Letty, returned to the car and Hannah made the long drive back. We drove to the hospital where I was due to stay until the formal paperwork and examination had been completed but they had already been told by Dr Wallace what had happened to me and said to Hannah that I need not stay as long as someone could look after me. She took me to her house and she and Donald very kindly gave me their bed for the night. I would be able to return to Phoebe's the following day and she also managed to get a couple of the nurses back to support me.

It was wonderful of Hannah to rescue me as it were, but she really did have no idea of what it was like to look after someone like me.

The grandchildren were wonderful and Elizabeth helped me go wherever I wanted to go, but it was beginning to be all too much for me and my mind went blank. I set off down the stairs in my pyjamas opened the front door and decided to go to the seaside and have a walk on the prom. It was only the fact that Patch, their dog, was barking so much that caused the children to look out of the window and see me going down the drive.

'Come on, Dad, where do you think you are going?' Donald asked when he caught up with me.

'I'm going to the prom,' I exclaimed joyfully.'To see Letty and Irene.'

'You can't, Dad, it's too late; everywhere's closed. Let's go in the morning.'

That was the first time ever that my son-in-law had called me dad and I remember it brought me round.

'What the hell am I doing here?'

'Don't worry, you just had a bad dream, you thought you were back in the home.'

I saw Hannah look at him in absolute amazement, and then go to him and kiss him. 'Thank you for being kind to my dad,' she said.

'Don't be silly, come on, let's all go in and get to bed, it's not morning yet.'

We trooped into the house followed by Patch who got the praise for looking after me and returned to bed. Thankfully there were no other disturbances until the morning when the children came in to see how I was.

Hannah telephoned her mother and told her she was taking me home, which sent her in a spin, making all the excuses possible; we haven't got this or that and it's too late for any nurse to be contacted, all of which Hannah countered and by lunchtime I was on the way back home.

At least Mrs Cripp was pleased to see me.

'Good Lord, David, you've lost weight and you are so pale. What on earth have they done to you? We'll have to do something about that, won't we?'

'It's a long story, Mrs Cripp,' Hannah said, answering for me. 'I'll tell you about it later. Can we come in now as Dad's getting cold?'

'Yes of course, I'm sorry.'

Phoebe suddenly appeared.

'It's not the end of the matter, Hannah, and I will not have you interfering. I'll decide what happens to your father not you. And I do have the power of attorney on my side.'

'Oh, Mother, grow up. This is not about you, it's about our father and what he has done for all of us and I'm going to make sure he stays in his house as long as it's possible. I suggest you see a copy of his will, Mother. He made it when he was of sound mind and you won't be happy.'

It was the second time Hannah had sprung a life-changing threat on Phoebe and the second time she didn't show any feelings.

'I'm not saying any more, Hannah, but you won't win this,' Phoebe said. 'Take him to his room, Mrs Cripp, and he can stay there.'

I was glad of it in any event as I was too tired to argue and too tired to think and now I welcomed the quietness of my room. Hannah had arranged for my nurses to be there and they were pleased to see me back, in particular Teresa. They soon bedded me down for the night and I had a good rest and felt a little better by the morning.

Over the next few days I began to recover and with the aid of my nurses and Hannah, and now Donald too, I did manage a slight recovery. They kept me busy with the mental exercises I needed to do every day, and I was beginning to get some of my speech and reasoning back. However, as I recovered, Hannah, who was like a terrier when she wanted to know what was going on, would not allow me to forget that I had mentioned Josh in front of her mother, curtailing the conversation. She knew something was not quite right and wanted a part of it.

I suppose if I had had Constance with me I could have told her there and then, but eventually, after prevaricating for several days, I told her.

'No wonder the bugger wants everything he can get his hands on, he's just like Mum,' Hannah responded.

I tried to tell her not to say anything, but when I got worked up, I'd lose control and often couldn't say anything. I just had to trust her judgement on that matter.

This knowledge made her more determined than ever to see justice done and to give me a better life and I was truly grateful for that.

The nurses, Mrs Cripp and Hannah began a programme of indoctrination; every few minutes they would show me a photograph of Constance and would ask who it was. They would talk about her, in particular Hannah who would remind me of the times we had had together. I didn't know then what it was for but I remember the day Constance came back. Hannah took me to the airport and as we waited at Manchester Arrivals, I thought I was going on holiday to France.

'Where's my case?' I kept asking.

'Don't worry, Dad. Everything is in hand.'

'Will we be late if we have to go back for it?' 'Honestly, Dad, don't worry.'

We sat down in the little coffee bar; Hannah keeping one eye on me and another on the screens on the Arrivals board.

'The plane is late, Dad, so we have plenty of time. Drink your tea and I'll read the news to you.' Suddenly she pulled out a few photographs. 'Who is that?' she asked me.

'Hannah.'

'Well done, Dad, it's me. Who is that?'

'Little Max.'

'Well done, Dad. Now who is that?'

I remember thinking for a while and then replied softly, 'It's Constance.'

'Well done, Dad,' she said and for the next few minutes I was tested to distraction.

After another cup of tea Hannah heard the announcement that Constance's plane had landed and told me that we wouldn't have much longer to wait.

'Where's my case?' I asked again.

'Don't worry, Dad, we are all right. Now, I have to go up there for a minute. You stay here and don't let anyone have my bag. Will you do that for me?'

'Yes,'

'Now sit there and hold on to the bag. OK?'

'Yes.'

Hannah went to the Arrivals gate and waited for Constance whilst I clung on to the bag like grim death. It wasn't long before I saw her meet a lady and being hugged for what seemed like ages and then the lady began walking towards me, quicker and quicker, until she was running.

'David, David, what have they done to you?' she asked as she squeezed me round my shoulders and hugged me. 'I'm so sorry, I won't leave you again,' she said, kissing me on my cheek.

'You can't have this bag. It's Hannah's,' I said, gripping the bag so tightly nothing would have prised it away from me.

'Oh, David, what have they done to you?' Constance repeated, obviously upset.

Hannah joined us and we sat at the table for a few minutes.

'Well are you pleased to see Constance, Dad?

'Yes,' I said softly. 'It's my Constance.'

Constance broke down and once again hugged me round my shoulders, placing her cheek on mine as she sobbed. She told me how much she loved me as her tears flowed. Hannah then joined in but hers were tears of joy.

'Let's go now, David. You're staying at my place tonight; in fact I never want you to go home to Phoebe ever again.'

Chapter 17

I felt shattered, but still could not get my past life out of my head and I remember I had been smiling, laughing and chuckling to myself as I realised that Phoebe had fallen hook, line and sinker into the trap that I had set for her all those years ago. I knew she would see me in hell even after just a few weeks of marriage. I knew she simply wanted the good life, which the business would give her.

I was still laughing, when the nurses came to give me my breakfast. It was causing them so much amusement and giving them so many unanswered questions and comments that it made me laugh even more.

'He's up to no good,' Sister Dorking said as she came on shift. She had been apprised of my behaviour through the night and was now keen to know what it was all about.

'Now, David, do tell us what you are up to; you've got us all on tenterhooks.'

She sat on my bed and began laughing, my laughter had been infectious and she had caught it. There we were, both were sitting on the bed laughing at nothing. I had forgotten what I had been laughing at and she was laughing at me laughing.

'Can you tell me yet'? she asked, bringing me back to earth with a bump.

I thought for a while, trying to get the words out and at last uttered, 'I've got my own back on the Dragon for what she has done to me,' and once again I started laughing.

'You're a terrible boy David, but I don't blame you.'

Someone was on my side, the sister must have seen what a cruel vicious cow Phoebe was and it gave me spirit, and I remembered how Hannah had been my strength.

I remember how she had the bit between her teeth when it came to revenge and gave no quarter, starting with the good Dr Banham. It gave me immense pleasure to listen to her relaying her antics. She made an appointment in Phoebe's name and waited with the other patients for her name to be called. Banham was surprised to see her, and even more so when she related what had happened to me. She told him she knew that Mrs Grice and Pat Davies had accepted money from him to worsen my condition in an effort to keep me in Sunnyridge, and furthermore the General Medical Council and the police were being informed.

'That's not true,' he said, beginning to sweat profusely, his corpulent frame turning to jelly. 'I only paid them for his keep, which your mother asked me to do. There was nothing wrong in that.'

'That's not true Dr Banham. I will call you Dr Banham for now but I feel it won't be long before you are struck off.'

It's quite clear from what they say on a tape recording I have that you and my mother were the ringleaders. They also say that there was a bonus in it for them if they were able to keep my dad there.'

'I had nothing to do with that. Whatever arrangements your mother made with them was nothing to do with me,' he said, his voice wobbling under the onslaught.

'How do you know my mother made any arrangements? Anyway, that's not what the recording states. It's quite clear you were the brains behind it and that you paid Grice and Davies for keeping my dad sedated so that he could not get out.'

'I don't know this Davies. I only know Mrs Grice and I only know her because she is one of the directors.'

'They have implicated you in every aspect of the scheme and we know from my mother's bank accounts that she has drawn out large sums of money in cash and that this money has been paid to you.'

'You can't prove that,' he stammered. 'You have no evidence at all and until you do I don't want to see you anywhere near this place or I will call the police.'

'Call them,' Hannah said, picking up the phone to give him. 'I'm sure they would like to hear things first hand. But anyway there's no need, our solicitor Terence Pendlebury is taking the evidence as we speak to the police and you will be hearing from them shortly. You lousy bastard – I hope you rot in prison,,' she added.

He slumped back in his chair as Hannah walked back into the waiting room, where she announced to the few patients who were there what he had done and that the police were involved. All left except one and she was deaf.

Phoebe had been very clever. There was no evidence any-where that she had been involved. Even the large cash withdraw-als didn't tie up with the money paid and although we all knew the real position she got away with it. Mrs Grice and Pat Davies were prosecuted for the misuse of drugs and pleaded guilty. But their mitigation was so clever that they received a supervision order for twelve months, but were not stopped from running the nursing home.

As for Dr Banham, he left the area as quickly as he came and we never heard of him again.

What amazed me about the whole affair was that Phoebe was totally unfazed by the matter. It was as though nothing had happened. She carried on as usual with her socialising, her shopping and even her scheming. It was incredible.

My sons had stayed away, worrying that I had been told about their little scheme with their mother to rob me of my last bit of life. The silly part about it is, I have never been one to hold a grudge, particularly with my family and I would have loved to have seen them, if only to let them know it wasn't important.

*

'Hello, David, Would you like a cup of tea?' the nurse asked. 'Come on, try and answer. Dr Percival is here to see you and he's going to have one with you.'

Oh god, who the hell is this now? Won't I ever get any peace?

Did I hear James was here, yes I did, here he comes.

'Hello, David, I've got some good news for you. You're going back home tomorrow.'

This was wonderful news; I hated being in hospital as I missed my Constance too much, but it was always the Dragon behind it and always at the first opportunity she would ship me out. I called it a hospital as it gave me the determination to get better, but it really was a hospice as they thought I was going to die. But, James said, I was going home tomorrow.

James had been a good friend and had retired years earlier, but he kept a few private patients on, to keep the little grey cells in order, as Hercule Poirot would say.

We chatted for a few minutes before he left and I went back to my thoughts and my past.

I remember after Hannah had argued with Banham and the case against Mrs Grice and Pat Davies was over. It was now Phoebe's turn to go on the attack and she had much to lose, but an awful lot to gain.

She had obviously consulted solicitors by the way she had started noting everything down and asking Hannah and Constance questions about the business, about the will and about the formal arrangements I had made for myself. We could easily smell a rat as Phoebe had invited Constance over to see her to discuss my well-being and what she wanted to do for the future. I wanted nothing of it as I was now content, but Constance felt we could at least find out what was in Phoebe's mind, particularly as I was now staying with Constance.

However, she had been warned once again about our relationship and in view of this and what she had discovered about the legal side, Phoebe decided that she would have it out with Constance to see what the real position was, but Phoebe being Phoebe, instead of being honest about the whole matter had to make excuses about her motives.

I could imagine what she was going to be like when we arrived and I was right. She was like a bull in a china shop.

'Come on in,' she said sternly as she opened the door and directed us immediately into the sitting room. 'I want a word with you.'

'Do you Phoebe, I wonder what about,' Constance replied.

Phoebe didn't waste time on formalities and was straight in with, 'It's about you, Constance, about you and the way you have had your hooks into my husband and have wheedled his money out of him. No, MY MONEY out of him,' she almost shouted. 'You have tricked him and used every trick in the book but it's mine. I am the one who has put up with the embarrassment of having him around; I'm the one who has lived with him all these years.'

Constance interrupted her, in full flight. 'You've missed a couple of things, Phoebe. You're the one who tricked him into marriage, you're the one who has tried to get rid of him and you're the one who is the embarrassment simply by the way you behave.'

I sat listening to them amazed that Constance put up with it without walking out, but she stood her ground.

'You won't win this, Constance. My lawyers tell me I have a good case to fight you.'

'Phoebe, darling,' Constance said, rubbing salt into the wound with her sarcasm, 'your lawyers are wrong and just want your money. Now listen and listen carefully. David would never see you destitute, in fact he would want the status quo, but if you continue this case against him then I will make sure you have nothing. For the record, I own sixty-nine per cent of Pennington's, having been given David's holding some years ago. David asked me to continue giving you your allowance, which I have done ever since. As for the other matters, Terence Pendlebury will deal with them as and when.

'I have left Pennington's to Hannah in my will, but I will probably give her the shares shortly and then it will be up to her whether or not you keep your allowance. Now that you have all the information you need to start the case, we will leave, but be warned, you will only make more trouble for yourself if you fight this.'

Phoebe was left in no doubt of her situation and after further discussions with her solicitor she was advised to let the matter drop and to be very careful, which she did, but not before she tried to get a formal agreement from Constance with regard to the retention of her allowance. Constance, however, would have none of it.

Phoebe now considered that she was divorced from me as I was effectively no longer part of her life and because of this she began an affair. I remember being told it was a torrid and steamy affair with Lance Williams, her personal trainer. He apparently spent many nights in my old home with Phoebe, who still wasn't bad looking for her age. It couldn't last long thought for there was forty years difference between their ages and I remember what I was like when I was his age. Young men want to try the experience of an older woman but few want to stay with it. With Mr Body Beautiful she hadn't a chance. He was a useful adornment at her endless parties which increasingly became a necessity for her. Phoebe wanted him at whatever cost and became desperate to keep him, it made her ripe for being taken advantage of.

People told Constance how she was behaving, how she would introduce him to her friends like some poodle on a lead. However, he was only in it for the money and everyone but Phoebe could see it. He didn't care short term what he put up with, as long as the sheckles came in and they did big style.

COME ON, GRANDDAD, HOLD MY HAND

The first con was when he told her he could no longer pay the rent on his flat and she persuaded him to go and live with her. He jumped at the chance and within a couple of days he was ensconced in her bedroom. But of course we had Mrs Cripp, who still kept in touch with us, giving us all the news and scandal. She told us that the relationship was very tempestuous and that after a few weeks he had moved into my old room. They still kept up the front of being lovers when they were in company but not on their own.

Lance then wanted to start his own health and fitness club and somehow persuaded Phoebe to invest £20,000 into the scheme, but she was running short of money and normally would have asked me, but now as she had power of attorney there was no need, she could help herself, but that account was now bare.

You had to admire her barefaced cheek as she came to see us at Constance's home pretending to be worried about my condition and simply came out with the demand.

'Constance, darling, I want to invest in Lance's new project and have run short of funds. Can you help me? It's only twenty thousand pounds.'

Constance was taken aback, but as I was in reasonable shape I whispered, 'Peace and quiet, give it to her.'

The moment the cheque was in her hands she was off, with hardly a word of thanks.

A week later we had a visit from the smirking Mrs Cripp, who was full of it. Lance had moved his girlfriend into the house and had begun to take over. He was even driving Phoebe's Range Rover; the poor woman was now becoming a bit of a laughing stock. However, Mrs Cripp told us how she had phoned the boys and asked them to call and help their mother but when they saw the size of Lance and discovered their mother had told him he could live there, they simply backed off.

Fortunately Mrs Cripp then decided to phone Hannah and even though she was at loggerheads with her mother, she would not allow this situation to go on and went to visit, accompanied by Donald, They arrived at the house, knowing that Lance and his girlfriend would be there and were ready to fight.

Mrs Cripp answered the door.

'You mother is in the study, Hannah.'

They walked to the study passing the sitting room where they saw Lance and Debra lolling on the settee with their shoes on.

'Wha d'ya want?' Lance asked in that awful manner as if he was the big man and owner. Hannah just stood in the doorway scowling at them.

'Wha d'ya want, I said.'

'Not you, lover boy, but just get your bloody feet off my mother's settee; in fact you can get your arse out of here,' Hannah replied.

'Who the fuck are you?' he asked.

'I'll tell you who I am, now do as she told you or I'll make you,' Donald said, again amazing me when I heard the story.

'You and who's army?' Lance added standing up flexing his muscles as only personal trainers do.

'Look, don't try your tough routine with me. You're all prick and no brain. So don't try it.'

Phoebe hearing the commotion came scurrying in and for the first time she looked her age. She had let herself go and looked ill.

'You're letting us live here aren't you, Phoebe dear?' Lance drooled.

'Yes, Lance,' she replied meekly; it was though the tables had been turned on her and she was now the subservient one.

'Well, I haven't,' Hannah said, 'and if you're not out of here by midday tomorrow you will be thrown out.'

'Well, you had better come with your army because I'm not shifting and nor are you, are you Debra?' She nodded, not knowing what to do, and with that he began kissing her and mauling her all over to which she reciprocated.

As they moved away from the lounge and into the study, Lance could be heard shouting. 'Ooooh, she's going to throw us out, oooh, I'm so scared.' This was followed by hoots of childish derision. He turned up the sound on his CD player to maximum, blasting everywhere with the noise as if to make a point.

Hannah and Donald walked into the study hardly able to hear themselves think to see Phoebe looking just a shadow of her old self. She burst into tears as she told them what had happened to her. She confessed that she had been a fool. She even confessed that she was trying to have a last grasp at youth, but now just wanted them out. She told them she was a prisoner in her own home and that they were always having parties with their so-called friends but they were just anyone who came and drank her liquor. All her other friends had stopped coming, there were no more bridge clubs and even Mrs Cripp didn't want to stay any more.

'Mother you are paying the price for all the bad things you have done and you don't really deserve any help, but no one should have to put up with this. Have you spoken to the boys?'

'Yes, but they are no more than useless.'

'Well, don't worry, we will sort it out tomorrow, just lock yourself in the room.'

They passed the lounge on the way out and Hannah reminded them of her threat.

'Don't forget,' she said sweetly. 'Twelve o'clock tomorrow, I'll be back.'

'Oooh, I'm so scared' Lance shouted.

The following day Hannah and Donald, together with a small van and a dozen men from Pennington's, turned up at Phoebe's. Lance and Debra were still in bed. They knocked on the door, which was opened by Mrs Cripp.

'Where are they?' Hannah asked.

'They are in your mother's room.'

They had even kicked Phoebe out of her bedroom.

Not another word was spoken as Hannah marched upstairs,

walked into the room without knocking and pulled the bedclothes off them. Debra screamed trying hard to pull the blankets back as she was naked.

'What the fuck are you doing?' 'Lance yelled.

'Just making sure you get out and you've got five minutes to get dressed or you will be out on the street naked. AND I have brought an army.'

'Oh, and by the way,' Donald added, 'this is not yours.' He picked up an envelope containing over five thousand pounds.

'Give it to me, it's mine.'

'Sue me, you snivelling little shit.'

Lance jumped out of bed to have a go, but a well-timed booted kick into his shin put paid to any retaliation.

'Try and take it, you robbing bastard,' Donald said, ready for anything else Lance might try to do. 'By the way, you've now got four minutes.'

The other men joined Hannah and must have looked a rum bunch as the two got dressed in seconds.

'Search them for keys and cash,' Hannah ordered.

The men did just that, but nothing else was found. They, together with all their stuff, were bundled into the van and driven to the tin shack that was to be the new fitness centre and dumped with all their belongings.

The driver, one of Pennington's security men, a massive fellow, leaned out of the van with the warning that if Lance or any of his friends went near that house again, every bone in their bodies would be broken.

Hannah gave a hundred pounds to each of the Pennington's men. Phoebe, meanwhile, kept the other money, treated herself to some new outfits and within a few weeks was back to normal. She was however thankful for what Hannah had done and saw the boys, except for Josh of course, for what they were.

Even though she had had this trauma and was faced with exclusion from her friends, she still did not want me around and quite frankly, I didn't want to go there as I preferred to be with Constance.

I was hoping she would leave things at that but not our Phoebe; her spending had become incessant as she tried to 'buy back' her friendships and apparently she succeeded to some degree, but this began to dip into her savings accounts. It was her own fault she was spending more than she received and with cap in hand she had to go to Constance to ask for more money.

Constance was a different kettle of fish to me. I would have given her the money just to shut her up and get out of my hair, but not her; Constance would ask questions. Why do you want it? Was there a cheaper alternative? I think she did it partly for devilment to punish Phoebe for all the troubles she had caused, but also because she herself was very careful with money.

Phoebe hated being dependent, but had the cheek to ask in a manner that suggested it was her right to have the money.

I remember on one day Constance told me she had refused and Phoebe had gone absolutely mad.

'Whose money do you think it is, dear?' she said haughtily.

'Phoebe, it's mine.'

She told me Phoebe went silent, too shocked to do or say anything and then suddenly she got up and flounced out saying, 'You can keep your money then.' But she was back a few days later demanding the same.

Phoebe was thankful for what Hannah had done and it wasn't long before my old house was up to scratch. But it was enormous for one old lady to be rattling around in. The lads had tried to talk sense into her, saying she should move to somewhere smaller, but they had failed miserably, so it was left to Hannah to sort things out. It all came down to money and status, of course, as it always did with Phoebe.

It was the first time in her life that Phoebe hadn't got her own way. And the experience with Lance had been terrifying, with the result she felt vulnerable, especially overnight, and was showing her age. I think she was now in need of company and experiencing for the first time what it had been like for me, for many years.

I was very lucky, I know Constance genuinely loved me more than anything and would have done anything in her power for me, but on one of our visits to the doctor, James gave me a few tests and confirmed I was a little worse, and then turned his attention to Constance.

'Constance you're looking very tired and I'm worried about you.'

'I am tired, James, I'm worn out. Can you give me something to perk me up a little?'

James turned to me as if to give me a warning.

'David, Constance needs a rest, I can see without examining her that she is overtired. You must try and let her ease up a bit or you will lose her.'

I don't think I understood what he was saying; I only wished that she would take it easy and not work so hard. She could have left it to the nurses but she always insisted she was there. She was now a shadow of her former self, but to me she was still the most wonderful woman in the world and the most beautiful.

As for me, I was now becoming very frail and could not cope with any worry or any problem. I was totally reliant on Constance.

James had been warning us for several months that Constance would have to go into hospital, for a bit of surgery, nothing terrible but it was necessary, with the caveat that if it wasn't done now, it would get serious. No one would tell me what it was on Constance's orders, as she did not want me upset, so I was blithely carrying on as though there was no real problem.

I had been almost normal for several weeks. Constance had kept the exercises going, both physically and mentally and felt that I would be in good shape for the two weeks we would be parted.

She had prepared me for this moment for several days, slowly educating me on what was going to happen, where I was to stay, and what I was to do if I was worried. She assured me that I will be all right and that Phoebe had been told what to do, but I knew in my heart that would never happen, and I think deep down Constance knew it as well.

James Percival had confirmed everything and was going to look in on me every couple of days, just to make sure everything was all right. She was now on a short waiting list to go in.

I remember we received the letter giving us the date when she would have to go and from that moment the worry set in. The following day, I could see in her eyes the moment we woke up that she was distraught. From then on matters became worse. I knew she didn't want to go, but needs must. Naturally I was shipped back to Phoebe's along with all my carers until she returned. I remember the welcome she gave me as we knocked on the door and she answered.

'Oh god, is it Wednesday already? I thought I had another day before being graced with your presence.'

I didn't reply, or even try, it was simpler to act dumb, but that was the worst thing I could have done, as she packed me off to my room.

'Come on, I'm not having you downstairs. Come on, get up,' she commanded.

I couldn't, nothing wanted to work. So she screamed for Peter, the gardener, who came running in as if there was some catastrophe.

'Peter help me get him to his room. I don't want him down here. What?' she asked, as she saw the look of disdain on his face at the way I was being treated.

'Nothing, Mrs Stephens.'

'Well, don't look at me like that.'

He didn't answer but looked at me with pity in his eyes. He didn't know half of what I had had to put up with.

'Come on, David, put your arms over my shoulders,' he said and those soft words of encouragement brought me back into the real world,

'Thank you, Peter, that's very kind of you. I can manage now.' I said it. It's wonderful to be able to communicate.

He let go and I was once again moving under my own steam.

'Now what were you saying, Phoebe?' I asked slowly.

'Oh just get out of my sight.'

I now slurred my words and could no longer speak properly, except on a very few occasions, so it wasn't even worth the attempt to respond to her.

Furthermore, I could only shuffle when I walked, which caused her to shout, 'Hurry up. I've got friends coming in a few minutes,'

What was worse for me now was that my memory was almost done for and it really was all I had left. I had to think of something, I had to remember what had happened in the past. It kept me alive. It was a way of talking, even if it was to myself.

It was strange, but I didn't want to die; I was prepared to suffer as long as I still had my Constance and I wanted to be near her.

My troubles were short lived. Hannah had taken me to the hospital every day to see her and on the third day we were told she was coming home the following day. Of course I was delighted, but concerned as they had been unable to find any- thing wrong. They emphasised that she needed a rest and I felt less concerned.

James when he heard was furious and complained to the hospital fearing they had missed the points he had made in his diagnosis, but as everyone assured him there was nothing wrong and she just needed rest, he was happier. The trouble was, she wouldn't rest.

I remember one morning I was terrified when I found her on the floor; she had fainted with exhaustion. I called for my nurse who took care of her and within a few minutes she was as right as rain. But then later in the day she fainted again. James was called and after a thorough examination he felt that she should be taken into hospital.

He really was a man of true spirit and understanding as he called the nurse and asked her to stay by whilst he told me that Constance was going into hospital again. I was distraught and quite frankly without the support of the nurse, holding me very firmly and kindly, I don't know what I would have done.

I remember Constance saying, 'I can't leave him in this state.'

And James replying, 'If you don't go now he will be left on his own for the rest of his life.' He then delivered a well-timed *coup de grâce*. 'Do you want to be left in Phoebe's hands? Because that's what will happen if she doesn't go.'

'Be brave for me, David. It won't be for long and I'll soon be back.' Constance then grabbed hold of me and we held each other tightly until the ambulance arrived, with me never wanting to let her go.

'Come on, David,' the nurse repeated, 'let Constance go now and I'll take you out so that we can see her off.'

Constance kissed me and it almost felt that it was for the last time. I knew she was also reluctant to let go as her arm seemed to cling to my body as she walked away, like some magnet holding on with its last bit of energy. She waved until the doors of the ambulance were shut and then I knew she was still waving as it slowly moved away. I stayed there until it was out of sight and even then I didn't want to go back into the house.

James had to inform Phoebe that Constance had been taken into hospital and it was simply a matter of hours before she had me taken into a home. She would not take any responsibility for me whatsoever. When I look back I think divorce would have been the best option. I know I would have married Constance and she would not have shirked her responsibility.

Even my nurses were annoyed at Phoebe's antics, telling her that they could cope easily with what facilities they now had at

Constance's, but it was no good, she was the next of kin and by the first evening I was shoved into this room where I am now.

The moment I entered this nursing home, I knew I had started to deteriorate very quickly. No one bothered to talk to me except Hannah and she couldn't be with me all the time. Phoebe made one or two duty visits, just to be able to say, 'I went to see David and he's fine,' because people were now seeing her for what she really was and she simply felt obliged to. She was still a schemer and it was only Hannah who would put a stop to her mother's ideas before they got off the ground, but Phoebe found other legitimate ways to punish me, like pushing me into this place.

She never really enquired about me, in fact there were occasions when she didn't actually come in to my room even though she visited the home; I also remember there were times when I pretended to be asleep so I didn't have to look at her. God what a terrible existence it was for the both of us.

My own nurses, who I had grown fond of, did come to see me, but Phoebe soon put a stop to that.

'I'll decide who visits my husband and you are not one of them,' and with that I was left on my own just to sit and stare; but at least I still had my thoughts. Thank god I had those, because they were my only company.

Phoebe even wanted me further out of the way and made arrangements to move me to another home. Of course she lied and told everyone it would be better for me as they had specialist nursing. Anyway for the first time ever the boys had had enough and told her to behave and they were not going to allow her any say in anything anymore.

I think I had been in the nursing home for three weeks when the nurse announced I had a visitor, it was Hannah and she came to tell me that she had seen Constance in hospital and that she was much better and would soon be home.

It didn't seem to register as things were becoming somewhat vague, but I could remember that I hadn't seen her for two or three weeks, because she had been taken into hospital for a rest.

I had been told she had been doing too much and Phoebe wouldn't have me back home so I was brought into here. My mind is wandering in and out of things and I'm having longer spells when there is nothing there; but I won't go until I have seen Constance.

'Dad did you hear what I have just said? Constance will be coming home soon, she's a lot better. Do you understand dad?'

I lifted my arm and smiled; she knew I understood. 'I want to go home,' I struggled to say.

'You will soon, Dad. Constance will be out very soon and you will be going home. Mum shouldn't have done this to you. I'll never forgive her for what she has done to you over the years.'

She stayed talking to me for a good hour before she had to go and I returned to my thoughts, always a little better after seeing her.

'David would you like a cup of tea?' the nurse asked as she entered my room; my smile was taken as yes.

I had always been fussy about my cups of tea throughout my life and it was terrible what I was having to put up with now; drinking it out of a plastic baby's cup was a dreadful experience; especially when some of the nurses spoke to me as though I was a small child.

'Now come on, David, hold it with two hands, then you won't spill it. Your doctor is coming to see you later on,' she continued. 'That's brought a smile to your face, hasn't it? Is he your friend?'

Of course he's my bloody friend and has been for years, but you know that, you've been told several times.

It was just after lunch when James arrived with his usual friendly, 'Hello, David, how do you feel today?'

It was always good to see him. He had been my only male company for over six years. In fact apart from the doctors at the Sunnyridge home he has been my only male conversation, so I valued him even more than just my good friend.

'David, I've got to talk to you. I really do need you to try and answer me,' he began with more than a tinge of sadness in his voice. 'David, I really have had enough of the way Phoebe behaves and her cruelty towards you. I just cannot let it go on any longer, it's been worrying me for years and now it is far too much for me to just let things drift along. There was no need for her to put you in here; the help you were getting at Constance's was more than sufficient and perhaps a damn sight better.

'I want to tell her what is in your will. It will be a big shock and make her realise what she is doing. Can I do that?'

I managed to muster a big smile and half a yes; in fact I started to laugh and from that he could see I was delighted.

I felt better after he had told me what he was going to do, but in reality I felt it was near the end. It's strange, I never thought I would know when my time was up but I do.

James was in a terrible state; I was sure he had begun to feel guilty that he hadn't tried hard enough to help me more and now in my last few days he wanted to make sure they were comfortable in spite of Phoebe.

'I went to see Constance this morning,' he said, 'and she will be home very soon and you can go back to her house. She really does look a lot better. I bet you'll be pleased to see her.'

I held my hand out to thank him for everything when he took it, I could sense that he was surprised how thin I had become and how cold I was.

'I'm going to retire soon, David. I need to wind down a little, but don't worry I will always be available for you, my friend, as long as you want me.'

I squeezed his hand, but there was hardly the strength in it to make any difference. Nonetheless James did feel it and smiled at me. God I knew I was coming to the end but I was determined to stay until I saw Constance again.

James talked to me for at least another hour before he left with a promise to return and let me know what Phoebe's reaction was.

I think I must have been a different person for the next twenty-four hours. It had given me a new lease of life to know that Phoebe was at last going to get punished for the way she had treated me over the last few years. I thought she would have at least learned some humility from the way she had been treated by Lance, but no, she was just the same.

It was my laughter that brought the nurses scurrying in, as I was remembering how we had formulated my will and the care I should receive and the consequences for Phoebe if she failed to carry them out.

'David what on earth are you laughing at? It must be something good for you to make this noise.'

I managed to say 'Phoebe' and then burst out laughing again.

'What has she done to make you laugh like this? I haven't seen you as happy as this since you arrived. Come on, David, try and tell me what it's all about.'

I really did try hard to communicate but I couldn't, it just ended up with laughter.

Supper arrived and for the first time for days I was able to feed myself properly, ate the lot and of course was heaped with praise from all the nurses. Then in spite of being bedded down for the night, I apparently chuckled the whole night through.

'David, settle down, you need to get some sleep, big day tomorrow, the specialist is coming to see you.'

They would always tell you something like that, to take your mind off what was keeping you awake, but I still had my mind working and I knew it was the usual bullshit. Anyway, I cat-napped all night and didn't seem to have any trouble waking up and eating my breakfast without help. I even felt like getting up but couldn't.

It was about ten o'clock when I heard this commotion at the nurses' station, I was sure I could hear Phoebe's voice. She obviously took no notice of the nurses and came thundering along to me.

'You bastard, you filthy bastard, how could you do this to me?' she shouted as she stormed into the room followed by two of the nurses who were trying to calm her down. She leaned over my bed and thumped me hard across the face in her temper.

'Get off him,' the nurse screamed. 'You'll kill him.'

'He can bloody die for all I care,' she continued screaming and with that made another lunge at me, but this time three nurses were on hand and she didn't get near.

Well, that did it for me; I must have been waiting for this moment for many years. I burst out laughing even though the nurses had noticed I was now bleeding profusely from the blow Phoebe had thrown.

*

'You better go, Mrs Stephens,' the sister said to Phoebe who had calmed down a little.

'Why, you bastard? Why?'

I could not think of anything else that would make the point strongly other than saying the word 'Josh'. She simply stopped everything and stared at me. I could now see the hatred of all these years together coming out in that look.

I did find difficulty in speaking but my mind was desperate to tell her I knew she never loved me and only wanted me for what she could get and what I did say she managed to understand and so did the nurses.

'I did not deserve to be locked away.' God I've said it. 'You've been cruel'

It was after that that I began to worsen and could not communicate at all.

I heard the nurses tell her she would have to leave and to give notice when she was coming again.

'I'll never come again. As far as I am concerned he is dead.' And with that Phoebe walked out and I never saw her again.

The nurse tended to my cut lip and told me they had phoned for my doctor and also Hannah, not telling them of the circumstances until they arrived. James was in shock as he blamed himself for Phoebe's actions. He could not stop apologising for the debacle and explained that over the years as my lifelong friend and doctor he had been tolerant for my sake with the way Phoebe had behaved, but now as everyone could see my slide into oblivion was quickening by the hour, he had simply had enough of her antics and the way I was being treated.

I managed to say 'thank you' and tears streamed down my face as he took my hand and kissed me on the forehead.

'David my friend, I am so sorry, that I put you through this.'

This emotional moment was curtailed as Hannah hurried to me, having heard what her mother had done.

'What the hell does she think she's doing to you, Dad? I'll make her pay for this,' she said, the anger oozing out of her.

I held my hand out which she clasped in both of hers. She was calm now and she too had sadness in her eyes. God seemed to be with me for the moment. Because I could talk and I could reason. I gripped her tighter and whispered:

'No, Hannah. Please leave it at that. I've won. I've got my friend James, I've got you and I've won the first prize: I got Constance.'

I turned away from them as I was too upset to talk anymore and both left together as I simply wanted to be left alone. My triumph seemed a little hollow now that I was alone and lost in thought. Did she deserve this? After all, the punishment I had meted out would last the rest of her life. But then I remembered all those little hateful things she had done and I suppose it was now the hatred that was helping me to keep going.

It's very difficult to remember what happened next. It's strange, I can remember many things in the past but the present is always difficult, but I've got to try. Come on, think man what happened next?

'Someone's here.'

'Good morning, David,' the nurse said as she opened my curtains. 'You've been restless again, look at you. Didn't you sleep?'

252

I mumbled something or other in reply which she took as no and then threatened to give me a sleeping draught.

'Let me straighten you up. Can't have you looking a mess can we, David?'

The excitement of the previous day had left me with a huge black eye, which was bound to cause some comment, but my nurse, the one which had obviously just become blind, couldn't see anything out of the ordinary.

'David I'm going to have to change the bed, it's a little damp. Have we had an accident?'

This is what really gets on my tits, god why have I said that? It's not a word I would normally use. Oh thank god it was only thoughts. Anyway, what's with the 'we'? Did you sleep with me last night and wet the bed? No! So why the 'we'? This is what I've had to put up with, everybody talking to me as though I was either daft or deaf and I have never been either.

'Nurse Williams can you give me a hand with Mr Stephens? I want to put him in the chair while I change the bed. We've had a little accident, haven't we?' she added in a silly little voice.

'I'm not stupid,' I managed to say.

'Oooh, we are a cross patch this morning aren't we?'

I just shut off. There was no point in even trying to waste what bit of energy I had left talking to them, and then of course Nurse Williams, the one who didn't need glasses saw my black eye.

'David, how did you do that?' she asked, pointing to my shiner.

I didn't have chance to answer before the blind one got in her two penneth.

'His wife came storming in yesterday and thumped him. Something about his will. He's not left her a penny.'

'For god's sake, he's not dead yet,' Nurse Williams added before realising she was talking about me whilst I was there.

'Sorry, David, but it's terrible.'

Yes, it was terrible and it started my thoughts once again. Had I been too hard on her, anyway it was too late now. She cannot change anything and I cannot as I'm not capable. Wait a minute, what are they're saying.

'I think we'll push the bed on to the balcony today. It looks as though its going to be lovely and it will do David good to be in the fresh air'

They're right it will do me good.

Well, that's just reminded me when Phoebe pushed me out of our bedroom. I can remember it as clear as daylight. She always, with me at least, treated sex like a duty and after I found out about Josh I could understand why. However, it was obvious she never wanted me, only the security I could give her, so within a few weeks of marriage she started to complain that she couldn't sleep and it was making her ratty and tired, particularly as she was pregnant. I had already started to go to work early in the morning and stay late at night, just to keep out of the way. She had a perfect excuse for single beds as I was waking her up at night or too early in the morning.

Anyway it suited me so I now had a single bed where at least I could get some sleep away from her.

It was a beautiful large room with its own huge balcony overlooking the garden, which faced south, so it had the sun all day long and because of its size we could have put ten beds in it and they wouldn't have been too many. Well, Phoebe wasn't satisfied with the standard three-feet single twin beds and suggested that we had larger ones. I was quite happy with mine, but next thing I found she had taken delivery of one four-feet wide bed and left me with my single and after a few days she told me it looked stupid and insisted that I move into my own room where I could have whatever bed I liked. My little three-foot bed was simply dumped in the room and left for me to organise. She would never include my room in any contract for redecoration. In fact it was though it didn't exist.

That was the last time I slept in the same room as her. I never went anywhere with her and from then on we simply began living our separate lives. So what the hell am I worrying about? She was a cruel bitch and deserves all she gets. The nurses can put me outside and I will enjoy it and I don't think I will give her another thought.

Well, it was a beautiful day and I was glad that after breakfast, they wheeled me out onto the balcony. I enjoyed my time in the sun. The huge umbrella placed above the bed kept me cool. I could hear the birds whistling to each other, the occasional chatter of the nurses as they wheeled some of their charges round the garden. I was so peaceful.

I managed to eat my lunch with the help of my nurses, sadly with hardly a word being spoken, and was then left again with my thoughts, but now I found it was difficult to remember. Things were becoming jumbled up and I could now feel the rest of me going. I knew it won't be long now and I'd be out of it forever. I was never really one for euthanasia, particularly now as I am only waiting for Constance. I know she will come, but is difficult when faced with this lot because all you have is pain and misery. No one can imagine what I have been through and what I am going through.

*

'David, Hannah's here.'

Good, my lovely Hannah. I tried to turn to look for her but found movement for the moment impossible.

'Hello, Dad, how do you feel?'she asked as she took my hand. The faintest little squeeze said it all and she just stood there looking at me, holding my hand and desperately trying not to cry.

'You can't go in there.'

Who the hell is my nurse shouting at now? Who else is not allowed to see me, because it will make me tired, I've got eternity to rest.

'No really, you mustn't go in. He won't know you. He doesn't know anyone anymore,' the nurse said as she came into my room.

'David.'

This lovely magical wonderful voice that I have been longing and living to hear, brought joy to my heart.

'My god, he does know you; he's smiling.'

'Of course he knows me. I love him'

Constance, I knew you would come; oh god, just give me a few more minutes. I want to tell her how much I love her, but I know I can't. I want to tell her how much I have missed her but I know I can't. Oh it is lovely to feel you holding my hand. Please give me strength just once more to . . . I'm doing it, I'm holding her hand. Is it imagination or am I squeezing it? I am, I am, I'm squeezing Constance's hand and she knows I can recognise her.

'I have tried to see you for days but have not been allowed to. You were too tired, too ill, having tests. I knew it was just a ploy to keep me away. Darling, I just had to see you, to let you know how much I love you and miss you and to tell you whatever happens you will always be in my heart.'

Kiss me, please kiss me as if it were for the last time. She understands my thoughts; I know she understands my thoughts. I've only remained living for this moment; to feel the warmth her lips touching mine and once again that tingling that races through my body as our lips touch.

She's lifting me up, this bag of skin and bones and holding me tight as though I was her treasured possession. Oh those lips again, that caress, that warmth. My whole body is coming alive. Oh I do love her. Tell her, tell her, come on you can do it; say I love you, say I love you. I can, I can I can 'I love you . . .'

Epilogue

Some people are embarrassed by Alzheimer's and have no more to do with the sufferer, even the closest of friends. 'I want to remember them as they were, not as they are now' is often said as an excuse to stay away. But they are the same people, they are just ill and it is now that they most need the support of those who are perceived to be their best friends or their closest relatives.

Many sufferers understand what is being said to them but simply do not have the capacity to communicate that they do understand.

I have tried to show in the simplest possible way the difference between Phoebe who doesn't have the patience to care and who constantly chastises David and the caring and loving Constance.

Phoebe talks at him and not with him, talks about him when he is there as though he wasn't, belittles him underming his self-esteem; she chooses to forget that he was the one who had made her privileged lifestyle possible. Now she is the one who cannot be bothered to look after him and shows him no affection.

Constance, on the other hand, loves him. She talks to him, has conversations with him, helps with his memory by doing exercises with him, ensures he takes medication, involves him in the decisions that have to be made; she always brings him into the conversation, especially when it was about David. She always tries to make him feel secure, something he values greatly, as all sufferers of this disease do.

There are thousands of sufferers of dementia and it is a

dreadful disease, not only for the sufferers but for all those around them who have to witness their loved ones, their friends or neighbours change before their very eyes into something totally different.

When things got bad and Constance wanted to attract David's attention, she would just touch his head; she would always use his name so that he wouldn't forget it. She got into his world, she would help him to do things and not do them for him, she would talk to him and not at him

Constance always made David feel as though he was needed she treated him like a human being and not an imbecile; she made him feel loved.

I have watched my friend of forty years disintegrate from a very astute, intelligent, well dressed man into almost the opposite. I have watched his wife struggle without help, trying to hold things together. She often went without sleep for nights at a time, trying to prevent him from leaving the house and wandering off to see his mother who died some thirty years earlier. I have seen him change from a man I saw as gentle, courteous who would never raise his voice to a woman and one who would never swear to a man who became foul mouthed and violent and even cruel to his wife. But this was not the fault of my friend or his wife; inside he may still be that person, he may still understand, but that dreadful illness has changed his personality and ability to respond, and there is nothing any of us can do, except give them support and try some understanding.